Dedi

To my husband, Marty, for his love, constant encouragement, unfailing good humor, positive outlook and, most of all, for *always* treating me like the princess we both know I am. Every woman should be so blessed.

To Mark

Happy 50th

Jan
+
Dean

Acknowledgments

The following folks helped make this book happen and are deserving of special thanks:

Barbara McNichol for her expert editing and "two thumbs up" for the early manuscript.

Carolyn Porter and Alan Gadney at One on One Book Production and Design. This extraordinary team does it all from editing to interior and cover design to marketing and more. They made the process a pleasure. I am particularly appreciative of Carolyn's enthusiastic encouragement, and above all, her kind patience with my constant changes and additions.

Dan Poynter for leading me to the above super shepherds.

Table of Contents

About the Author — 7
The Putting Old on Hold expert!

Foreword — 9
Take action now to stop the aging process.

Preface — 13
You don't have to get "old" — ever.
I am the expert and I have spoken!

I Tell It Like It Is — 15
Because I'm preachy and
I know everything you need to know to Put Old on Hold.

Introduction — 17
I've been there and done that (the aging thing),
so you can trust what I say is true and will work for you.

Agenda — 21
Listen up — Here's the game plan. Yep, this is what it takes.

Health — 23
Gotta be in tippy-top condition to Put Old on Hold. You can do it!

Retirement — 77
Don't go there if you want to Put Old on Hold.
Here's what to do instead.

Attitudes, Tools and Advice — 101
Here's the right stuff to Put Old on Hold, babe! It works if you do.

Terrific Tips to Put Old on Hold — 147
Yes, they are terrific!
I know because I've road tested every one of them.

Resources — 153
Information to help you Put Old on Hold — good stuff
to get you moving in the right direction.

Index — 157
To help you find every pearl of wisdom.

Barbara Morris at age 72

About the Author

Barbara Morris is a graduate of Rutgers University College of Pharmacy and works full time as a retail pharmacist.

Early in life she became convinced that signs of "old age" associated with the aging process, not just heredity, were the result of lifestyle choices, and as such, could be manipulated and controlled. Now over age 70 and having the physical and mental characteristics and abilities of someone many years younger, it is clear her beliefs about how to achieve agelessness were right on target and are paying off even better than she had hoped.

As Barbara enters what she calls her Second Life, she is dedicated to helping Boomers and others realize their dream of retaining characteristics of youth – a goal she insists is absolutely achievable. She contends anyone willing to take steps she has taken can replicate her success.

Barbara enjoys reading, writing, crossword puzzles, and fantasizes about becoming a professional ice skater when she grows up. Her husband Marty, a former college professor now into his second career as a pharmacist, has maintained his love for research and, as a result, Barbara insists he is the smartest man in the world. As expected, traditional retirement is not part of their life plan.

Their many blessings include a daughter, two grand-children and a home in Southern California, the closest place to paradise on earth – except when the earth shakes.

Foreword

Take Action Now To Stop The Aging Process

Over the past decade, scientists have made tremendous advancements in the field of anti-aging medicine. Breakthrough discoveries are being made on a daily basis. From the decoding of the human genome to the use of pluripotent stem cells for tissue and organ regeneration, scientists are beginning to control the biological aging process on a cellular level.

Over the next twenty years, these advancements will radically change the face of medicine and dramatically improve the quality of life for aging Americans. Yet despite all of our scientific advancements, the most important factor in human longevity continues to be a healthy lifestyle.

Of course, the benefits of healthy lifestyle are well documented and well publicized. And yet despite all the information on diet and exercise, over one-third of all Americans are now considered clinically obese.

That's a frightening statistic when you consider the fact that obesity contributes to three of the leading causes of death in the United States. That includes heart disease (31.4%), cancer (23.3%), and stroke (6.9%)

The actions that you take on a daily basis directly control your body's physiological rate of aging. Your dietary habits, exercise routines, stress management capabilities, and joy of life will either cause your body to become weak and feeble or help your body grow into a vital, energetic, and youthful version of your current self.

Understand that lack of action is an action. If you are serious about maximizing your longevity and physical quality of life, you must start taking positive steps to nourish your brain, vital organs and tissues while simultaneously strengthening your muscles, joints, and bones.

A great place to start is by adopting the techniques outlined in Barbara Morris' newest book, _Boomer's Really Can Put Old on Hold._

This is the best new anti-aging book available. Unlike the majority of books on this topic, Barbara Morris' book was written with the average reader in mind. Her book outlines a program that is extremely easy to follow. Her experience as a pharmacist has taught her how to transfer her personal counseling skills into book form. When reading this book for the first time I often felt as though I was standing at the pharmacy window being advised by my local expert.

The single most important point Barbara makes is how critical it is that you take personal responsibility of your health. Regardless of how wonderful your health care providers are, you are ultimately responsible for the health of every cell in your body. If you nourish and protect them, they will serve you well. If you deprive and abuse them, they will degenerate and decay. The choice is yours.

Barbara points out that no generation understands these facts better than Baby-Boomers. After watching their parents and grandparents struggle with debilitating diseases such as cancer, diabetes, and Alzheimer's disease, boomers have increasingly made the decision to take a proactive approach to health and wellness.

Today, Boomers represent 28% of the U.S. population. At seventy-six million strong, Boomers represent the largest single sustained growth in population in the history of the United States. The massive wealth, power and influence controlled by this generation give them the ability to drive change in the medical industry. This generation understands that the body, mind, and spirit all play a role in health and wellness and will demand that physicians diagnose and treat them as a whole, rather than as a sum of their parts.

I believe that over the next two decades, Boomers will ignite a revolution in the medical field. Integrative wellness will become the norm. Health care will become extremely proactive, incorporating cellular diagnostic techniques to monitor biochemistry throughout your lifetime.

Modern western medicine will be combined with Eastern philosophies to treat your entire being. Customized nutritional supplementation will emerge to provide your body with the precise formulation of nutrients needed for your individual biochemistry.

Thousands of clinical studies have shown that today's most common diseases are caused by the lack of proper nutrient intake. Scientists have shown that supplementing your diet with essential vitamins, minerals, herbs, and hormones can help you maintain a youthful physiology and prevent most illnesses from developing. By giving your body the optimal level of important nutrients, you can reduce symptoms and dramatically improve your overall health. Clearly, when it comes to longevity, healthy nutritional habits are essential.

In countries like Japan, where diet consists mainly of whole foods that are unprocessed and lower in fat, records consistently show lower rates of obesity, heart disease, osteoporosis, memory loss, menopause, and breast, colon and prostate cancer. Typically the people in these cultures are much physically younger than their chronological ages. This is proof positive that adopting healthy lifestyle habits can dramatically improve longevity.

Of course, the primary objective in anti-aging medicine is not just to extend human lifespan, but rather to increase the number of active, healthy, and vital years lived. As president of Longevity Labs, my focus is on improving our client's entire quality of life. Our goal is to help people enjoy their "senior years" with the same physical abilities and function as people in their thirties and forties.

Over the years, I have read countless books from self-proclaimed anti-aging experts. *Boomers Really Can Put Old on Hold* truly is the first book that provides a straightforward program for stopping the physical and mental signs of aging. The strategies contained in this text have been proven to keep both mind and body feeling young and vital.

Barbara Morris has personally proven that the aging process can be controlled. She radiates more vitality and energy than women two decades younger. She is truly a shining example that the aging process can be controlled by maintaining a healthy lifestyle, regular activity and a youthful attitude.

I personally challenge you to adopt the easy-to-follow lifestyle techniques outlined in her book. Making these simple changes in diet, exercise, stress relief, and nutritional supplementation can help add years to your life and life to your years.

~ **Brandon Barnum**
President and CEO
Longevity Labs Inc.
www.LongevityLabs.com

Preface

This is the second in a series of *Put Old on Hold* books to help Boomers (those born between 1950 and 1964) and others realize their dream of being "young forever." While preserving physical attributes of youth is challenging, staying young mentally and maintaining youthful characteristics is definitely doable today.

"Old Age" is a state of mind *and* a culturally assigned chronological number. It used to be 65, then 85. Now we have more centenarians than ever. But reaching the 100 mark is no longer a reliable indicator of "old age." In 1999, in an average month, 50,000 people 90 and above were in the workforce – in a society that views "old" persons as incapable of productivity on a par with younger people. Indeed, the concept of "old age" is changing and improving rapidly, and in ways never dreamed possible even 25 years ago.

Gerontology gurus are finding it increasingly difficult to clarify when old age actually occurs, or even what it is. Their search for definition is difficult because old age is not a disease. It's not a number; it's not a condition – it's a choice. To a great extent, a healthy individual can control mental and physical signs of "old age" by staying aware of personal changes, practicing aggressive maintenance and just refusing to allow age-related decline to gain a toehold.

Two distinct models for aging exist in our society: The dominant traditional "senior culture," which is a state of mind and a way of living that invites decline and dependence, and a growing "ageless culture" consisting of those who choose to Put Old on Hold. The latter adhere to a new way of living and thinking that defies decline and dependence while promoting healthy, productive, ageless longevity.

I believe it's possible to Put Old on Hold indefinitely. I'm doing it; I've discovered some "super keys" to healthy ageless-ness and share them in this book. Warning: *Boomers* Really Can *Put Old on Hold* is not for content retirees. It's for those intent on living seamlessly and productively with lifelong, youthful élan.

I Tell It Like It Is

Some of my friends say I'm preachy – like a geriatric Judge Judy. Some friends, huh? Such an appraisal offends me greatly because, as you can tell, I am positively more charming than her Honor. Well, maybe you can't tell just yet. Trust me, I am more charming, especially when I preach.

Here's my excuse for preaching – if and when I do. Telling people what to do is a way of life for me. I'm a pharmacist and constantly give advice in response to questions such as, "What can I take for my backache?" or "I've got this hacking cough that keeps me up all night – what's good for it?" or " Does that stuff they advertise to perk up your love life really work?" No kidding – people assume I am an expert on just about every ailment or problem a human can experience. Since I am not a physician and not licensed to practice medicine, I usually make several appropriate suggestions, preach if I think it will help, and leave the final decision to the customer.

I unabashedly admit to preaching and telling it like it is when it comes to aging. Far too many people get old too fast and it shouldn't happen. Every fiber of my being believes the various types and levels of decline typically seen with advancing age are *not* inevitable. In spite of irrefutable evidence, in spite of expert knowledge – in spite of it all – I maintain you *can* control the quality and momentum of the aging process. But how can I say that in the face of the obvious? Just look at older people all around in various stages of decline – how can I make such an assertion and expect to be taken seriously?

There are and always have been certain "truths" known to us that result from observation, assumption, tradition and the pronouncements of experts. Such "truths" are irrefutable. But are they always? Here are some "truths" that have been proven false:

- The earth is flat. If you get to close to the edge, you will surely fall off.

- Crops fail and animals become sick and die because of spells cast by evil witches. Burn the witches and all will be well.

- A high fever is indicative of too much blood in the body. To cure the patient, apply leeches to the body to suck out "excess blood."

The above were "truths" given the understanding, knowledge and prejudices of the times in which those beliefs existed. To have spoken against them was heretical. Yet, it has since been proven the earth is not flat, crop failures and plagues are not the result of evil spells and "blood letting" practiced during the Middle Ages is now considered total quackery.

Many more untouchable "truths" held in bygone times now reside in the realm of the ridiculous. A lot of "truths" of our time relating to aging, and seemingly carved in stone, deserve the same fate. As you read this book you will become aware of many detrimental contemporary "truths," and you will discover how you can avoid and overcome their negative effect on your health, happiness and longevity.

Please understand anything I say should not be construed as medical advice. I give my opinions (often controversial), what I believe, what I think, what I know, what works for me or for others, but not medical advice.

An important final note: Please know I care about *you*. You are not a faceless entity to me. Although I may not know you personally, I do know you are a precious person who deserves a healthy, happy, long, and productive life. You *can* Put Old on Hold if you really want to, and that's telling it like it *really* is.

Introduction

Welcome to the one and only "crash course" for Boomers and others who want to be young forever. Believe me – it can be done and I'll help you do it. It is my goal to give you the very best tools and information you need to Put Old on Hold. It's not difficult when you know how.

As this is written I'm 70 plus. My actual age doesn't matter. Normally, I do not to reveal my age and suggest you don't either. It's just as personal as your bank balance, and you wouldn't reveal those numbers to just anyone. By declining to reveal your age, you can live with greater freedom, avoiding some of the limitations our culture places on known chrono-logical age. For example, if your age is not known and you appear younger than you are, you will not likely hear depressing comments or questions such as "You are too old to do that" or "Why are you still working at your age?" (If you are ever asked the latter question and you are a woman, your stock answer should be that you have child support and alimony payments to make. Then watch the reaction. It's fun.) The only reason I'm telling my age now is because you need to know that I know what I'm talking about. I'm sure you'd prefer to learn how to Put Old on Hold from someone who is actually doing it, rather than from a forty-something "expert" who has poured over scientific journals, interviewed a multitude of old

> I'm sure you'd prefer to learn how to Put Old on Hold from someone who is actually doing it, rather than from a forty-something "expert."

folks and thinks he or she has all the answers. Experience beats theory!

My take on chronological age is this: It's an accounting of time gone by. It's a useful identifier for some legal purposes but our culture goes far beyond that, attaching undue importance to age. We assign parameters of behavior and being to each decade, thereby controlling, for too many people, how much or how little they can get out of life. Rebels who choose to live outside the bounds established for acceptable behavior for a given chronological age often have a hard row to hoe. Admonitions to "act your age" can devastate latent ability and shoot down achievable aspirations that could change the world. Chronological age has no relationship to ability or state of health. I believe it is far more important and humane to focus on biological or physiological age – how well the mind and body maintains itself over time. This is the *real* age that matters, and I promise, you have enormous control over it. You **can** Put Old on Hold.

> Chronological age has no relationship to ability or state of health.

As I've already mentioned, I'm a pharmacist. I work full-time in a supermarket pharmacy. I plan to work indefinitely because I believe voluntary retirement, except in certain circumstances, is an anachronism in the world in which we now live. My work is very stressful but challenging and I value it for these reasons:

1. It keeps me sharp and aware, which are highly youthful characteristics and key elements in Putting Old on Hold. Dealing with the public helps maintain my mental edge and realistic perspective of the world.

2. It forces me to always look my best. It means I wash my hair, get my nails done and have work clothes

clean and pressed when I have to, not when I feel like it. Regular, systematic maintenance helps Put Old on Hold, and having a job that forces me to keep up personal grooming is better than having a nagging mother who keeps reminding me to do what I know I should do.

3. It's a great reality check for how I'm doing. I'm at an age when custom and tradition say I should be "slowing down" or "losing my edge." When I see I can work faster and more accurately than a pharmacist 30 to 40 years younger, I *know* I'm Putting Old on Hold. It's great for my self-esteem.

4. It allows me to help people in ways that would be impossible if I were doing anything else – if I were retired, for example. As I think about different lifestyles I could be living, it reinforces my belief retirement would be a waste of precious time for me and a loss for others. That's not arrogant – just realistic.

5. It gives me the opportunity to work with some remarkable young people. I cannot stress enough the importance of "multi-generation" exposure. For an older person, interaction with a young person can be a gift that helps maintain a balanced outlook on life. I'm tempted to say the value of being around young people is not about adopting their behavior, but that's not entirely accurate. In the workplace, for example, mature youngsters often act as exquisite teachers of patience, kindness and extraordinary common sense when dealing with difficult people. More than once, young co-workers have bailed me out of a potentially volatile situation just with their "unflappable cool" – a hallmark of youth I constantly strive to emulate because of its human relations value in many situa-

tions. This modeling works wonders when applied appropriately.

6. It allows me to live relatively financially stress free. I don't have to pinch pennies as many seniors do; it's a blessing and I'm grateful. My heart is heavy for those existing on Social Security and little else. I feel especially troubled because many poverty-level seniors have the capacity to work, which would ease their financial situation and generally improve their quality of life.

7. Best of all, my job gives me an intimate, bird's eye view of the behaviors, thinking and lifestyles of people of all ages. What I see confirms my theories about aging and reinforces my resolve to keep doing what I'm doing.

Agenda

I'll be covering three basic topics as they relate to Putting Old on Hold. Understand, adopt and incorporate the essence of these simple yet powerful concepts into your thinking and behavior on an ongoing basis, and you can easily Put Old on Hold. If you do, all of your life, and most particularly for all of your Second Life after age 60, you will experience an incredible, enviable quality of life few people achieve. Believe it will happen; act on it and authentic agelessness will be yours!

Health

The condition of your health and your ability to maintain it in an optimum state – plus your determination to constantly improve it will affect your ability to Put Old on Hold. Nothing is more important. I will also address dependence on unnecessary medication as it affects your ability to Put Old on Hold.

Retirement

Whether or not you retire plays an important role in your ability to Put Old on Hold. Do people still want to retire? Of course they do, even when they shouldn't.

Attitude, tools and advice

Having an independent, tough, contrarian mindset about aging and using the right tools to develop agelessness determines how successfully you Put Old on Hold. And it doesn't hurt to try the tools and listen to advice from someone who's not only "been there and done that," but is doing it right now and will continue to do it.

Health

Benefits of Good Health

Your health is your most important asset and possession. Acquiring and maintaining it must be a consuming, priority activity. Your health is more important than money, sex, power or relationships. The flip side of the coin is that, with optimum health, you can have it all. With great health, money is better, sex is fantastic, power is more awesome and relationships are what you choose to make them. Optimum health provides liberation beyond measure. It is a power trip that boggles the imagination. Excellent physical and mental health will truly enable you to Put Old on Hold indefinitely. I guarantee it.

> Excellent physical and mental health will truly enable you to Put Old on Hold indefinitely.

With super health, you have dominance over the quality of your life and even your longevity. If at age 60 you have exceptional health, if you are physically and mentally strong, then you have an opportunity to begin a brand new Second Life far more rewarding than the first. I know it's possible because I'm doing it and you can do it, too.

At a healthy 60, you can be so much smarter and wiser in so many ways because you finally understand what's important and what's not. Liberated from youthful concerns and anxieties, you are free to do what you've always wanted to do. When I say you can have a Second Life, that's exactly what I mean. It's an unprecedented gift you can enjoy if you play your cards right early enough in the game. In your Second Life, you won't have to muddle through the terrible teenage years and suffer through another "mid-life crisis" all over again. The youthful struggles of "getting there" will be a thing of the past — but you will use valuable past life experiences to grow on. This Second Life will epitomize the essence of Martin Luther King Jr.'s proclamation, "Free at Last! Free at Last!"

> Putting Old on Hold is not work; it's an exciting challenge and an opportunity to do what you want to do with your life, regardless of chronological age.

Putting Old on Hold is not work; it's an exciting challenge and an opportunity do what you want to do with your life, regardless of chronological age. It's being able at 60, 70 and beyond, to feel like a kid, looking great, being your most productive, looking forward to the future and saying, "Wow! This is fantastic! Why isn't everybody doing it?" Because you are reading this, consider yourself one of the lucky ones who will reach a destination called Old on Hold. I have the road map and directions to get there because I know the way, intimately. There will be no detours and no cops to give you a speeding ticket for wanting to get there in a hurry. So stay with me!

Your health:
Whose responsibility is it?

Don't ever lose sight of the truth that your health is your most precious possession. I'm going to remind you of that repeatedly because it's vital to internalize health consciousness as a

> Adjust your attitude until you can joyfully embrace your health as your first and foremost concern.

preface to everything you think and do. Adjust your attitude until you can joyfully embrace your health as your first and foremost concern.

How do you begin to take responsibility for your health? First, recognize and accept your health as *your* personal responsibility. That should be a given, but not everyone sees it that way. So I'll clarify: It's not your spouse's responsibility, your parents' responsibility, your children's responsibility, the government's responsibility or your doctor's responsibility. It's your responsibility.

One day, a woman picked up prescriptions for high blood pressure and cholesterol, then asked if I could ring up a couple of romance novels. Each book was about two inches thick, so it appeared she spent a lot of time reading. I wondered if she took as much time to learn about her medical problems, so I asked her. She replied, "Oh, that's my doctor's responsibility. He's being paid to worry about it."

Wrong answer! Her doctor is surely a very caring person, but should she expect him to worry about her health? I don't think so. Her health isn't the doctor's responsibility.

In contrast, another customer came in to pick up a prescription for her high cholesterol and, before she would take it, she wanted to talk about side effects. She had done some research and discovered the medication the doctor had prescribed was potentially harmful to the liver. She asked me to comment on her findings.

Rather than tell her what I knew from my recollection, I showed her the information sheet the manufacturer provides with every package of medication. It's very comprehensive and includes all the potential side effects. ("Insider information": When you have a prescription filled, always asks the pharmacist for the "package insert." You probably won't understand 90 percent of what it says, but you will understand the description of side effects.)

After reading the list of potential side effects, which included, as she knew, the possibility of liver damage, she said, "Never mind. I won't take the medication if it's okay with you. I've lowered my cholesterol before with diet and I can do it again. It won't be fun, but at least I'll have a healthy liver."

That's taking responsibility. But what if she is unable to bring down her cholesterol to an acceptable level this time – what then? Chances are she will, having done it before, but if she can't do it again, then common sense says do what you have to do using medication. But she will have improved her diet and she will have tried to take personal responsibility. This is a person with the ability to Put Old on Hold.

> Taking responsibility means not smoking.

Taking responsibility also means not smoking. If you smoke, I'm not going to preach to you about giving it up. You know better than anyone all the reasons why you should quit. Just remember you can do anything you put your mind to. Yes, you were encouraged to smoke and even tricked into it one way or another – with irresponsible health or safety claims, or relentless advertising that led you to put that first cigarette in your mouth. But look, you made a choice. Even after the first puff made you sick as a dog, you chose to continue. Regardless of why you began, get a defiant attitude in gear and refuse to see yourself as a "victim" or having a "disease." Decide to be an overcomer. You can do it.

If you want to quit smoking and want my advice about what helps, here it is: Patches work for some, not for all. You really must want to quit in order for them to work. I've seen people use patches and continue to smoke; they rationalize they are inhaling less tar and nicotine! Nicotine gum is okay but some people become hooked on it and think that's also better than inhaling. Well, maybe it is, but nicotine in any form will not help you Put Old on Hold. Then there is prescription medication called Zyban™. The exact same drug is marketed as Wellbutrin™ and used as an anti-depressant. Does Zyban™ work? I know of no success stories, which doesn't mean it doesn't help. It may be worth a try if your doctor agrees it's right for you. Interestingly enough, many insurance plans will not pay for Zyban™. Is that crazy, or what? Maybe they figure it's cheaper for them if you develop lung cancer or emphysema.

Integrative/alternative physician Julian Whitaker, M.D., offers another way to quit smoking in his newsletter, *Health & Healing* (January, 2001, Vol. 11. No.1 – more info in Resources section). It includes taking a recommended medication, drinking lots of water and taking vitamin C when the cravings become intense.

Last but not least, there is "cold turkey" which many people simply can't endure. One reason it is so difficult to stop smoking is that nicotine stimulates production of serotonin – the substance that makes you feel good. When you try to quit, the serotonin drops and you become moody and irritable, you crave sweets and snack food and wind up gaining weight. That's when you run to the doctor whose only solution, if you have tried all the other would-be remedies and they have failed, is to put you on an anti-depressant as a last ditch effort. And that may not help, either.

But here's the best way to kick the habit: Optimize your health every way you possibly can. You may find your craving for tobacco diminishes as you improve your health and get on a

> You may find your craving for tobacco diminishes as you improve your health and get on a regular exercise program.

regular exercise program. Taking this approach – along with whatever support you want to try – will make quitting smoking a lot easier.

I know I said I wouldn't preach to you about quitting, but I want to give some facts from the National Center for Health you may not be aware of. Consider the following if you smoke and are on the fence about giving it up:

⊗ Each cigarette smoked burns away 8 minutes of your life.

⊗ Smoking a pack a day translates to losing a month of life each year; smoke 2 packs and you can kiss goodbye 12 to 16 years if you are a lifetime smoker.

⊗ Smoking compromises the immune system so severely that it takes 3 months to reverse the damage to the immune system once you quit.

⊗ Smoking one pack a day depletes 500 mg. of vitamin C – more than most people absorb in one day.

⊗ Cigarettes elevate the carbon monoxide level in the blood, which competes with oxygen so ruthlessly that it takes the circulatory system six hours to return to normal after just one cigarette.

Do I hear someone saying, "Yuck! Pooey!" That's not the half of it. Smoking sucks – the life out of you.

> Smoking sucks – the life out of you.

Take responsibility for your health

Doctors don't know everything. Some know more than others, yet nobody knows it all. They all want to do their best but often it's not enough because, in medical school, students are trained to use diagnosis, intervention and medications to save lives. Nutrition and prevention – the most basic aspects of maintaining health – are given little consideration. Although that is slowly changing, it's not happening fast enough. Basically, that means you should look out for yourself.

> Doctors don't know everything.

Given the above reality, if you have a health problem, you owe it to yourself to learn as much as possible about your condition so you can become an informed participant in your care and treatment. Please understand I'm not suggesting you become a "know it all" after a limited amount of study, then attempt to tell your doctor what to do. The key is "informed participation," which will empower you to make intelligent choices about treatments your doctor may suggest. Bear in mind you don't have to accept any treatment your doctor recommends. Time and again, customers tell me they don't agree with their doctor's evaluation or treatment of their condition but go along with it because "he's the doctor." I personally feel it's suicidal to hand your body over to someone, however highly credentialed, and say, "Here's my body. Do with it what you will." Never forget – it's your life, it's your health and it's your body, so take responsibility for it.

> The key is "informed participation," which will empower you to make intelligent choices about treatments your doctor may suggest.

Therefore, since doctors are trained to focus not on prevention but on treatment of symptoms, you can expect your doctor will attempt to "fix" your problems with medication.

You have high blood pressure? A pill will bring it down. High cholesterol? A pill will lower it. There may be little if any discussion of the role lifestyle choices may play in contributing to or alleviating the problem. However, when you become an informed participant in your health care, it may be possible

> When you become an informed participant in your health care, it may be possible to work together with your doctor to find more prudent, non-medication solutions to your problem.

to work together with your doctor to find more prudent, non-medication solutions to your problem. By the way, if your doctor resists your informed participation, do the obvious. Find a doctor who will listen to you. Your doctor is not God, but if that's the way you see him or her, bite the bullet and find another medical deity. There are lots of them out there. Some are better listeners and more open minded than others. Some will even pray with you if that's your inclination!

If you don't have a significant health problem, now's the time to make certain one doesn't develop, especially if there is a history of a particular illness in your family. I don't subscribe to the theory that just because your parents had cancer or diabetes it will be your fate. Perhaps your parents didn't live a particularly healthy lifestyle, even though they probably thought they were doing "all the right things." They didn't drink or smoke, but they did eat the disastrous All American diet, unaware of the role it might have played in the condition of their health.

Facing the reality that certain ailments tend to "run in the family;" and recognizing the role of genetics and heredity, I'm nevertheless convinced paying attention to lifestyle choices can break the chain of many seemingly "inherited" diseases such as diabetes, high blood pressure and even cancer. When it comes

> ....paying attention to lifestyle choices can break the chain of many seemingly "inherited" diseases such as diabetes, high blood pressure and even cancer.

to health, I'm just not a fatalist. You have far more control than you think you do.

The importance of lifestyle

Dr. John W. Rowe, president of the Mount Sinai Medical Center in New York and chairman of the MacArthur Foundation Research Network on Successful Aging, maintains that how well you age is 70 percent lifestyle and 30 percent heredity. If he is correct, and I believe he is, then clearly lifestyle choices matter – a lot.

But I think Dr. Rowe is very conservative with his lifestyle/heredity ratio. I believe how well you age is closer to 80 percent lifestyle and 20 percent heredity plus non-identifiable environmental causes. As longevity researchers continue to uncover what contributes to healthy longevity, Dr. Rowe's lifestyle/heredity ratio might get even better. The challenge is to find and implement those choices that promote optimum health and the longest possible duration of youthful characteristics.

An even greater challenge is to determine which lifestyle choices among those identified as most likely to help Put Old on Hold work better than others. I believe generally unknown or not widely accepted "super keys" exist, which unlock super benefits. For example, what are the benefits of a restricted calorie yet super nutritious diet? Even though the value of a low-calorie, high-nutrition diet is not yet scientifically established, mounting evidence shows the idea has merit. Personally, I feel better when I don't eat a lot. I choose food carefully, paying attention to nutritional value. When I eat a high-protein power-packed breakfast and drink a lot of water during the day, I can work all day without feeling hungry. My mind is clearer and I have lots of energy. If my stomach starts to gurgle, I have some nuts that tide me over until I come home from work. Dinner is often a bowl of oatmeal laced with ground flaxseed, topped with fruit and soy milk. It's yummy!

In China, people tend to live a long time. They eat a grain-based diet, using meat sparingly as a condiment to flavor the grain. They also restrain their eating. Perhaps because of economic conditions, children are taught to eat until they are almost full and, as part of good table manners, to take less of what they really love. Over the years I've worked with many Asian pharmacists. I've always marveled at the simplicity of their food choices and how little they eat compared to Americans who can't seem to function without consuming tons of grease and red meat.

Another "super key" to good health and longevity may be fasting. A concept as old as the Bible, it is now gaining acceptance among mainstream medical practitioners. Dr. Stephen Sinatra, in his newsletter, *The Sinatra Health Report*, March 2001, maintains that fasting, in addition to other health benefits, doubles growth hormone levels compared to not fasting. Human growth hormone (HGH), if you

> Another "super key" to good health and longevity may be fasting.

are not aware, is a substance you have when you are young. It is responsible for youthful characteristics. Over time, its production slowly declines, resulting in the usual signs of advancing age. It's possible to restore youthful qualities with injections of supplemental human growth hormone, but it is not without risks. HGH is known to cause cell division and turnover, possibly putting anyone who takes it at an increased risk of cancer. If fasting a day or two a week can naturally boost your own production of HGH, it seems rather miraculous and well worth a try. You can learn more about HGH in *Grow Young with HGH* by Dr. Ronald Klatz. He gives resources for HGH, anti-aging therapies and a list of physicians who specialize in anti-aging medicine.

By the way, fasting doesn't mean you go hungry. You can fast on juices as well as water to keep you up and running. Fast on a day you don't go to work or do anything too strenuous. If you have a juicer, a bag of carrots, some celery, fresh fruit and whatever else you like, you can have an enjoyable, beneficial fast. But fasting is not for everyone. If you are diabetic or have other health problems, check with your physician first.

> Fasting doesn't mean you go hungry.

I believe another "super key" is the underestimated value of something as basic as water consumption. An amazing number of people don't like water. Yet, your body is 80 to 90 percent water. Every cell depends on having enough water to function optimally. If you don't constantly replenish the water your body uses to process food, eliminate toxins and keep it operating as intended, it's reasonable to expect you will have difficulty maintaining even minimal good health. While the jury is still out on the benefits of a restricted calorie diet, the value of adequate water consumption is undeniable. It's one of the best-kept secrets of those who maintain agelessness. They are the people who remain like beautiful juicy plums that will not shrivel up.

> If you don't constantly replenish the water your body uses to process food, eliminate toxins and keep it operating as intended, it's reasonable to expect you will have difficulty maintaining even minimal good health.

Health Care Realities

Managed health care

Managed Health Care is pretty much the norm today and health care rationing is on the horizon. To successfully Put Old on Hold, it's important to understand how this could affect you and what you can do to avoid becoming a "victim" of either managed health care or health care rationing.

There is growing disenchantment with health care maintenance organizations or any kind of third party insurance. Members of HMOs see consumer costs rising and the quality of health care declining. It's not your imagination that prescription prices are going through the roof – even if you have insurance. Co-pays are already obscene, and if you think it is bad now, get ready for what is on the way. More expensive drugs will continue to appear on the market. They are advertised directly to consumers, creating a demand for them. Those suffering from arthritis, for example, see a compelling ad on TV or full color ad in the newspaper for a new pain medication and become convinced it's the answer to their prayers for relief.

"Direct to consumer" or DTC advertising is extremely expensive and adds astronomically to the cost of medications. DTC is powerful; it achieves its intended goal by driving consumers to the doctor's office demanding a prescription for the latest magic bullet. The doctor complies with a prescription for the advertised medication, presumably first having read or at least listened to information supplied by the drug manufacturer's representative.

> "Direct to consumer" or DTC advertising is extremely expensive and adds astronomically to the cost of medications.

The patient, feeling victorious because he has a prescription in his hand for the latest and greatest medication, has visions of a "cure" dancing in his head and hurries to the pharmacy to claim his "treasure." And there he comes face to face with reality. The patient's HMO doesn't want to pay for the new drug, maintaining that older, less expensive medications work as well. (And a lot of them do, truth be told!)

If the doctor really wants the patient to try the new medication, he may have to spend time trying to convince the HMO why his patient needs the latest, most expensive drug on the market. If the HMO refuses, as it often does, and the patient really wants to try the new drug, the patient pays full price out of pocket. It's not uncommon for a 30-day supply of a brand new wonder drug to cost several hundred dollars. Then the distraught patient wails, "Why does this prescription cost so much?" Part of the answer is the expensive and convincing DTC advertising that sent the patient scurrying to the doctor's office to ask for it in the first place!

How expensive is DTC advertising? Pharmaceutical companies spent $833 million on TV ads and $460 million on print ads in 2000[1]. Breaking those figures down into more familiar numbers, companies spent $152 per lead on TV ads and

> Retiree drug costs are expected to rise 20.9 percent in 2001 because of rising patient demand for specific medications.

$318 per lead using print media – that's the cost of driving a consumer to a doctor to ask for a prescription. That sounds like a lot of money just for a lead, but not to worry – if the lead turns into a customer, he or she will help recoup the expense for the company. And it will happen. According to a *Reuters*[2] report, retiree

1 "Internet Drug Ads Retain Their Low-Cost Edge," *iMarketing News*, February 12, 2001

drug costs are expected to rise 20.9 percent in 2001 because of rising patient demand for specific advertised medications.

What if the patient pays full price for the costly panacea, but it fails to produce the desired relief or causes side effects so severe that he or she must stop using it? It's a lot of money down the drain – a serious concern not only when it hurts you, but your budget as well, especially if you must survive on minuscule Social Security checks.

Sooner or later, however, HMOs begin to pay for the latest and greatest medication but only after securing a satisfactory financial arrangement with the drug manufacturer or government. Or, failing that, patient co-pays increase and/or the cost of insurance goes up. It is not uncommon to see prescription co-pays in the $50-$75 range. That may seem high, but it's not if the full price for the drug is several hundred dollars.

As the expression goes, there are no free lunches. In the medication game, the cost of advertising is a factor in the price of a prescription. The unwary patient helps foot the bill. To put it another way, snookered with enticing, expensive DTC advertising, the patient, desperate for relief, falls for the bait, then is forced to help pay for the bait that reeled him or her in.

In spite of the effectiveness of DTC advertising, it appears this form of marketing is not highly regarded by some segments of the public. To test DTC acceptance, www.Medscape.com conducted a 15-day poll asking, "Do you favor or oppose direct-to-consumer advertising of prescription drugs?" Of 3,416 total responses, 31 percent were in favor and 69 percent opposed. How many respondents were medical professionals is not known, but it doesn't matter. DTC produces positive

---

2   "Drug Benefits Costs to Jump 20% in 2001," *Reuters Health,* October 23, 2000

financial results for advertisers and that's what counts to the pharmaceutical companies, at least for now.

To be fair when talking about the high cost of prescription drugs, I need to make clear other cost factors that come into play. For example, U.S. pharmaceutical companies give away an estimated $8 billion in free samples each year, an amount growing eight percent a year. Drug companies give them to doctors who give them to low-income or indigent patients. It's one thing to be aware of the sampling give-away and another to see it in practice. Recently, while in my doctor's office waiting for my appointment, at least six drug manufacturer's sales reps came in with huge shopping bags filled with medication samples. It reminded me of kids at Halloween with their trick-or-treat bags. As they gave their scripted sales pitch to the nurse (not the doctor) at the desk, they scooped out handfuls of free samples. Knowing what medication costs, I saw a lot of money given away – as if it were candy. Another thing that surprised me – a couple of the reps appeared very young – perhaps just a couple of years out of high school. There was a time when a drug company hired nothing less than a licensed pharmacist to visit doctors on the assumption they had the training to professionally interact with doctors and answer technical medical questions. As I listened to the young reps give their canned presentations, I wondered how much they really knew about the products they were promoting.

In addition to office give-aways, most drug companies have direct "patient assistance programs" that provide one-to-three-month supplies for low-income or indigent patients. These programs gave out $500 million in drugs in 1998.

Another reason for the high cost of medication is the astronomical amount of money poured into research and development of many promising drugs, which more often than not don't work as projected and are abandoned. When a new drug is shown to be effective in trials, it must first pass through a lengthy and extremely expensive process of approval (or rejection) by the Federal Drug Administration (FDA) before it can be marketed. That adds to drug costs, also.

Take care of your health and you can stay off of the medication merry-go round, maybe not entirely, but more than you might think possible. Freedom from taking medication is a blessing with too many ways to count; it's a priceless prize to pursue.

> Take care of your health and you can stay off of the medication merry-go round, maybe not entirely, but more than you might think possible.

Health care rationing

Health care rationing is closing in, and the older you get the more momentous this issue becomes. I've heard about health care rationing for many years; in practice, it exists right now. For example, if you need or want a particular medication (as in the example above) or a surgical procedure, whether you get it may be up to a committee that weighs the pros and cons of the necessity in your situation.

I recently read an article that expressed the urgency to understand the kind of pressure you will be exposed to as you age. The title of the article is "Is it Justifiable to Ration Healthcare on the Basis of Age?"[3] The opening paragraph states: "Since healthcare is not a limitless resource, there is little doubt that rationing is required." Please note the warning – "there is little doubt" that rationing is required. Until recently, talk about rationing was expressed as "may be" or "could be."

---

3 Drug & Therapeutic Perspectives, 16(3):14-16, 2000. ©2000 Adis International Limited

The article says it could be argued that those who have lived to a certain age (perhaps 70 years) have already lived most of their expected lifespan, so priority should be given to those who have not yet lived so long. It also suggests that society has a greater duty to prevent the death of the young rather than the old.

It's not my intention to argue the merits or demerits of health care rationing, although if you are on the 70 plus side, it seems like a terrible idea.

The point I want to make is this: If you take responsibility for optimizing and protecting your health early on, then health-care rationing and doing battle with cost-conscious HMOs or any insurance entity should not significantly concern you.

I truly believe that with appropriate lifestyle choices and enhancements, the need for a lot of expensive medical care can be reduced considerably. You can't eliminate all health problems from your life; you can't eliminate the unexpected. Certainly, "bad" things happen to "good" people who do all the right things. But the odds of bad things happening can be substantially reduced with intelligent lifestyle choices, which in turn will significantly improve your ability to Put Old on Hold far longer than you ever thought possible. Believe in your own ability to take responsibility for your health and make intelligent lifestyle choices, then do it!

> Believe in your own ability to take responsibility for your health and make intelligent lifestyle choices, then do it!

Why be afraid?

Scudder Investment Services surveyed 5,000 Boomers and found 82 percent feared they would have deteriorating physical health. Not having enough money worried 66 percent.

Fear of declining health is indeed rampant and due in part to two things: *What you experience and observe, and social conditioning.* You see people all around whose health is declining, so it seems inevitable it will happen to you. Then you have the purveyors of gloom and doom who give credence to your observations.

In just one example of the latter (and there are many more), a newsletter published by an HMO states, "A certain amount of short-term memory loss is normal, starting as early as one's mid-40s." Where is the scientific documentation? Where is the absolute evidence? Imagine a Boomer, who feels insecure about his or her health, reading such a dire prediction. It can become a self-fulfilling prophecy. It gives permission to let down one's guard, to invite decline by believing "I must be getting old" when memory lapses occur, which everyone experiences. After all, "they" said it is going to happen so you might as well accept it. No, you are not going to accept it without a fight. You are going to defiantly and intelligently work at improving your memory and do what you need to do to Put Old on Hold. Learn how to protect your brain and your memory by reading *Brain Longevity* by Dharma Singh Khalsa, M.D. It will give you hope and, most important, the tools you need to take responsibility for your mental well being. (This book is listed in the Resources section.)

> You are going to defiantly and intelligently work at improving your memory and do what you need to do to Put Old on Hold.

I have worked with many conscientious, bright young people. Typically, they go to school, are involved in sports and have a "significant other." They have a lot to think about. And guess what? When there's a ball game or a hot date coming up (trust me on this) – they sometimes forget what they are supposed to do on the job. Of course they apologize, but never once has any one of them blamed a memory lapse on his or her youth. And why should they? After all, everyone forgets now and then; it has nothing to do with age. Young people focus on

> After all, everyone forgets now and then; it has nothing to do with age.

youthful concerns while older people worry about taxes, their errant kids, their marriage, or whatever – and the accompanying stress often results in fleeting forgetfulness. Regardless of age, it's reasonable to expect things to "slip between the cracks" once in a while. Don't sweat memory lapses. When they happen, let them happen without fear you are losing it, and without berating yourself for getting old. Until you are diagnosed with Alzheimer's or dementia, stay strong in your belief in your ability to remember whatever you want.

Fear of decline accosts you in so many ways. I've seen an ad on TV in which a Boomer-aged woman says she isn't afraid of growing old, but she is worried she won't be able to afford the cost of medication. This very powerful conditioning is negative and destructive. The unspoken message says you WILL need medication as you age and that both decline and deterioration accompany aging.

It would be wonderful if public service announcements assured people if they take responsibility for achieving optimum health, they will need to worry less about the cost of health care. Healthy people do not rely on the health care system to stay well. Great health is not the result of visits to the doctor or taking medication. Great good health is achieved by what you do for yourself, day by day, year in and year out. Yes, lifestyle choices count.

> Great good health is achieved by what you do for yourself, day by day, year in and year out.

How do you take responsibility?

Educate yourself!

But how? Where do you start? Please do not protest you are not smart enough to take responsibility for your health. "It's too complicated." I hear that a lot. That's nonsense. Maybe you just don't want to be bothered? If you are able to hold a job and function well in your everyday life, if you can remember all kinds of sports trivia and statistics, and you surf the Internet, you are smart enough to learn anything you want to learn. Today, self-education is easier than ever. There is more than enough information on the Internet to enable anyone to become expert on any given subject. There is no longer (if there ever was) an excuse for ignorance about anything. If you don't know how to surf the Internet, the library is an excellent resource.

> There is no longer (if there ever was) an excuse for ignorance about anything.

Here are other learning opportunities:

- Health and lifestyle sections of bookstores abound with well-researched books by writers, researchers, medical doctors, alternative health gurus and just ordinary individuals who have found their own cure for one thing or another.

- Magazine racks bulge with a variety of health-related publications.

- Health food stores offer books by alternative practitioners of every kind as well as free magazines. While the magazines are primarily advertising vehicles, they usually contain well-researched, documented, reliable information.

- Excellent newsletters written by medical doctors are available by subscription. Many doctors have their own informative websites. (Information about relevant websites and newsletters is included in the Resources section of this book.)

A word of caution: If you are just beginning your quest for knowledge, don't believe everything you read. Read everything, but question everything. Beware of following one "guru." Eventually you will come to a place where you will be able to make good judgments about what and what not to believe. Even then, as you continue to learn, your thinking will evolve and your discernment will improve. Always stay open to new information regardless of how "expert" you may become.

> Always stay open to new information regardless of how "expert" you may become.

Another way to take responsibility for your health is to find a medical doctor who practices alternative or integrative medicine. Alternative medical doctors rely less on traditional medicine and more on natural treatments that focus on elimination of the source of a given problem, rather than just treatment of symptoms. They have a totally different mindset about what it takes to be well. They tend to encourage full involvement of patients in their health care regimen.

A medical doctor who practices integrative medicine uses the best of traditional medicine and alternative medicine. He or she is more middle-of-the-road than a dedicated alternative physician. Whether the physician is alternative or integrative, his or her mind is more open than a traditional one and is more likely to respect your thoughts about what type of treatment is appropriate for you.

If you belong to a health plan that allows a choice of doctors, call each doctor on the list and ask "flat out" if he or she practices integrative medicine. You may get lucky and find one. (How to find integrative or alternative practitioners is included in the Resources section of this book.)

Stamp out food abuse

The very best way to take responsibility for your health is to control what you put in your mouth. Start by stamping out food abuse! You say you don't inflict food abuse on the one and only body you will ever have? Of course you do. Everybody does at one time or another. But you are doing everything right, you protest. You are, of course, eating the accepted All American diet and what's wrong with that? A lot.

> The very best way to take responsibility for your health is to control what you put in your mouth.

You can't treat your body like a garbage can for 50 years, stuffing into it the worst elements of the "All-American" diet and expect to Put Old on Hold and run like a Mercedes for the next 50. Sure, George Burns made it to 100 apparently on wine, women and song, but he was the exception. His "super key" to longevity may have been his outrageous sense of humor. However, for most people living on the traditional All-American diet, Putting Old on Hold is not going to happen with just the help of a sense of humor.

You can change your diet if you really want to. You weren't born loving pizza, greasy burgers, high calorie or "pseudo" foods. Once you make a commitment to your health and resolve to make lifestyle changes that will enable you to Put Old on Hold, you *will*

> Once you make a commitment to your health and resolve to make lifestyle changes, you will be able to Put Old on Hold.

eagerly want to eat what's good for you. And you will treat your body with respect. You will learn the magic and joy of eating to live instead of living to eat.

Food abuse – what is it?

Food abuse is ingestion of "stuff" non-stop over a long period of time. That "stuff" does not promote good health but contributes to poor health. You know the culprits: grease, fried anything, refined sugar, processed, empty calorie, non-nutritious drinks and snacks. And don't forget pickled, preserved, "fresh" embalmed or processed meats contaminated with bacteria and in the process of putrefaction.

Speaking of culprits, I was walking by a food court in a shopping mall and took note of what people were consuming. One plate in particular caught my eye. On it was a mound of deep brown, deep-fried whatever – looked like a pile of turtle turds. The person devouring it was obese and in a wheel chair. When was the last time you had a plate of greasy, indescribable yummies? Don't do it again – I'll have you arrested by the food police and committed to a vegetarian health spa for recovering grease-a-holics! You don't think grease is addictive? One of my relatives says he has to go to a fast food place at least once a week for his grease fix. He's kidding, I hope, but ingesting a lot of grease, much of it rancid, is a way of life for a lot of people.

Everyone makes poor food choices once in a while. That's not going to destroy your health or impair your ability to Put Old on Hold. "Once in a while" is not the same as day in and day out, year after year of constant, unrelenting food abuse.

What are signs of food abuse?

After eating a greasy hamburger or a hot pastrami sandwich or any concoction laden with grease, preservatives and an assortment of chemicals your body doesn't know how to process then your stomach complains, you are guilty of food abuse. When that happens, listen to your body and stop the abuse. Don't continue to eat what your taste buds love but your stomach hates.

> Don't continue to eat what your taste buds love but your stomach hates.

Don't believe commercials on TV that suggest you can eat all kinds of ingestible material masquerading as food and that you can pacify the resultant painful symptoms by popping a pill. That is insane. You can beat up on your body with food abuse and try to cover up your abuse with pills for just so long before you develop other problems related to your food abuse. Your liver will start acting up. You will experience intestinal problems. Your gall bladder will rebel. Your arteries will start to clog. Your cholesterol will pile up.

If you want to Put Old on Hold, ignore TV commercials that encourage you to trick your body with a pill. It doesn't work.

Food abuse – why do people do it?

All of us are victims of what I call the "All American" diet. Or the "Corporate America diet." Or the "supermarket diet." It's a diet that includes the sum total of ingestible products created and sold by corporate food makers. It's not all bad – you just have to know the difference between what's good for you and what's not.

These ingestible products become the basis of the diet most people consume. I refer to these products as "ingestible" because I don't consider a lot of them real food. They are manufactured products resulting from scientific tinkering in corporate "kitchens" or, more accurately, laboratories. Good natural ingredients are processed and re-engineered to taste terrific and provide emotional satisfaction. If one crème-filled donut or savory greasy chip isn't enough for you, then the food scientists have achieved their goal. To make it even more tempting, these engineered ingestibles are advertised on TV by loved and respected celebrities or cartoon characters. Obediently, viewers rush out to buy these "food" products.

Enticing, full color ads in Sunday newspaper ads support TV advertising. Larger-than-life depictions of potentially palate-pleasing products have your mouth watering in anticipation as you clip the coupons to buy a product. Once you put it in your mouth, you're hooked. Your taste buds are screaming for more. However much you eat, it's never enough. You have to chow down the whole box or bag. Isn't science wonderful? Sure it is, but what comes from Mother Nature is much better.

Supermarket temptations

Enticing food ads would be meaningless without a place to buy the products. Take a look at the layout of your favorite market and start with the mile long aisle of shelves groaning (on both sides) with "breakfast cereals." Just about every home in America starts the day with puffed, popped, flaked or shredded "cereals." I must tell you, so-called "breakfast cereals" really bother me. I can't understand why people continue to buy them, or what makes them so appealing other than the sugar content. When my daughter was small, after watching a TV commercial for corn flakes one day, she asked me to buy them. I said "no" but she was relentless and I finally gave in. Guess what? She didn't like them and never again asked for corn flakes or any other pseudo cereal product.

People go to work on this stuff; a couple of hours later, they feel hungry for real food. With their blood sugar in such a slump it's impossible to concentrate, so it's time for donuts and coffee as an energy pickup. But the sad thing is that kids are sent off to school, loaded with enough carbohydrate from "breakfast cereal" or toaster pastries to send a rocket into space. When they can't sit still or concentrate, behavioral specialists decide the sugar-shocked kids have Attention Deficit Disorder (ADD). The cure is narcotic drugs that turn them into obedient zombies, at least until they become teenagers. Judging by the number of prescriptions I fill for Ritalin™, Dexedrine™ and Adderall™, one would think there was an epidemic of maladjusted or brain-damaged children. Wouldn't it make more sense to try an improved diet first? If that doesn't work, at least it would get kids started on a course of sensible food choices. It's never too soon to start to Put Old on Hold with sound nutrition. After all, you begin to age the moment you are born.

When I was a child, ADD had not yet been invented. I don't recall classrooms in chaos with kids unable to behave or concentrate. Children sat in their seats and learned what the teacher taught. If a child decided to demonstrate "attention deficit" behavior, he or she was sent to the principal's office until the behavior dissipated. At that time, sugary, lifeless breakfast cereals were not a staple in every home. It was the Depression and breakfast was likely cheese spread on whole wheat bread. From a nutrition standpoint, it was a lot better than what most children now eat for breakfast every day.

> Read labels and decide for yourself if the high carbohydrate, low protein or high fat and minimal vitamin content of the products you eat each morning are worth the price.

Although the nutritional content of "breakfast cereals" has been bumped up considerably in recent years, nevertheless, much of it is still "pseudo food" with not much more nutritional value than shredded or flaked cardboard or puffed Styrofoam. Read labels and decide for yourself if the high carbohydrate, low protein or high fat and minimal vitamin content of the products you eat each morning are worth the price. When you do read labels, you will surely conclude that instead of starting off the day with a bowl of expensive sugary, soggy shredded "whatever," you might do better with nutritious whole grain bread (which hasn't been denuded of its vitamin and mineral content) slathered with cottage cheese or almond nut butter and a drizzle of honey. You might even consider eating oatmeal, which cooks faster than you can pop a pastry into the toaster. You'll then have something nutritious at a fraction of the cost.

> Please, shop carefully. Read labels. Spend your money on real food that will help you Put Old on Hold.

Then there is the mile-long aisle beckoning with all the snack "food." The cakes, the donuts, the chips, the sodas. The deceptive "low fat" but high carbohydrate nutritionally worthless goodies. Please, shop carefully. Read labels. Spend your money on real food that will help you Put Old on Hold.

Some people (not you, of course) actually forego "breakfast cereal" and, instead, have donuts and caffeinated soda or coffee for breakfast or other junk too horrible to mention. Just stop at your local convenience store to pick up the morning paper and watch what people on their way to work buy for their breakfast. Constant sugar and caffeine overload is really abusive. Chronic coffee and caffeinated soda junkies and donut dunkers can forget about Putting Old on Hold. They will be lucky if they make it through a day without feeling like a wrung-out dishrag.

> Chronic coffee and caffeinated soda junkies and donut dunkers can forget about Putting Old on Hold.

> An ingestible manufactured or processed product (or any product, for that matter) must produce a profit. That's the primary concern – not nutritional value, not your health, but profit.

The point is this: Take into consideration how our "free enterprise" system works when it entices you into making diet choices that may not be in your best interest. Love yourself enough to fight back! An ingestible manufactured or processed product (or any product, for that matter) must produce a profit. That's the primary concern – not nutritional value, not your health, but profit. And that's fine; profit makes our system work. We are the envy of the world and rightly so. Our system produces such extraordinary abundance, yet we are not as healthy as we could or should be. However, our incredible variety of choices allows individuals to make intelligent decisions about food. You just need to be *aware* and *think* when deciding what you will put into your mouth.

I see shopping carts piled up with a load of red meat, processed, fatty foods, chips, sodas, frozen pizzas and similar tongue-tickling delights; several loaves of bread that rival Kleenex™ for whiteness, softness and nutritional value; breakfast cereals devoid of significant food value; nutritionally worthless donuts and a head of iceberg lettuce. It doesn't take a rocket scientist to understand why medications are needed to control blood pressure and high cholesterol.

It is sad those with medical problems who eat like this on a regular basis don't understand the connection between their condition and what they consume. They believe they are eating a "good" well-balanced diet because they eat a variety of ingestibles. Besides, how bad can it be – just about everyone eats the same thing so it must be okay. No, it's not okay, and yes, just about everybody does eat the same corporate-created diet. The result is an epidemic of obesity, high blood pressure, high cholesterol, gastrointestinal troubles and other problems apparently without a cause.

Here's the reality: If you live on a nutritionally unsound diet day in and day out over many years, your ability to Put Old on Hold will be difficult and probably impossible. If you are an abuser, decide to change your diet *now*.

At this point, if you are a Boomer or younger, I bet I know what you are thinking: "Give up what I love to eat for a benefit I may not realize until way into the future? You have got to be kidding! Besides, what everybody considers good food is social grease – events go better with familiar food. Businessmen make lucrative deals over traditional greasy lunches. People fall in love over burgers and fries. Macaroni and cheese and hot dogs keep families together. Give it all up for salads and soy burgers? No way. I feel great. Nothing wrong with my health. I'm going to be just fine." Sorry, you won't be fine. You'll be sick and old just when you could be starting a healthy, vigorous Second Life. You can't get away with it if you want to Put Old on Hold. So I'm going to repeat what I said: If you are a food abuser, decide to change your diet right now!

> If you are a food abuser, decide to change your diet right now!

Supplements

You are inviting debilitating old age with what you eat. You are compromising your ability to Put Old on Hold. Are you doomed? Of course not, particularly if you mend your ways early enough. The body is incredibly forgiving and often responds miraculously to tender but aggressive

> The body is incredibly forgiving and often responds miraculously to tender but aggressive loving care.

loving care. And you can do a lot to compensate for your abuse by taking supplements.

Why supplements are necessary

It's not easy to turn away from what you've been happily eating for most of your life and become a "health freak." To do so means you are fighting not only deeply ingrained habits and preferences of your taste buds but family custom and tradition. But you must do it. A food consumption study conducted in the mid-1980s by the U.S. Department of Agriculture evaluated the food intake of 21,500 people over three days. Not one met the recommended daily (RDA) for the top ten nutrients. And the RDA set by the government is unrealistically low. Worse than that, diets have not improved since then.

The desire to want to eat a more nutritious diet is not made any easier when you ask a traditionally trained physician if you should take a vitamin supplement. Chances are he or she will say, "If you eat a well-balanced diet you don't need vitamin supplements. You are throwing your money away." I would like to ask doctors who give this advice to explain their definition of a well-balanced diet. They probably live on the same All American deficient diet – or even worse. Most likely they don't know beans about optimum nutrition, because they lack training. Medical school gives short shrift to nutrition and wellness education. As I mentioned earlier, that is slowly changing. Harvard University has a new division of Complimentary and Alternative Medicine, and it is reported that many other universities are implementing alternative medicine programs, including a Program in Integrative Medicine at the University of Arizona Health Sciences Center. Even hospitals are getting into alternative treatment. Beth Israel Medical Center in New York has a center that offers homeopathic and chiropractic therapy. Herbal medications for depression are offered at the University of Pittsburgh Medical Center. It's a drop in the bucket, but it's progress, so let's be grateful and hopeful for the future.

This "new awakening" may help explain why more traditionally trained doctors are recommending supplements. It's becoming more acceptable. If there is one thing medical practitioners fear, it's the scorn of their peers. They consult with each other a lot about what's okay and what's not. A mainstream doctor doesn't want to be considered a "kook" of any kind by colleagues. A good example is what happened to Nobel Prize winner Linus Pauling. He was a respected and celebrated anti-war activist until he made known his controversial views on vitamin C. After that, his status as a credible scientist was diminished in the medical community. Although his research on vitamin C has been validated, he never regained his revered position among many of his peers.

> Supplements are definitely needed by those taking prescription medications.

Supplements are definitely needed by those taking prescription medications. For example, oral contraceptives, which many younger Boomers take, deplete the body of vitamin B-6, folic acid, vitamin B-12, vitamin C and the minerals zinc and magnesium. What is the significance of these depletions? For one thing, depletion of vitamin B-6 reduces synthesis of serotonin, which can result in depression and anxiety. Can that explain why so many women on oral contraceptives also take antidepressants? Depletion of vitamin B-6 also reduces synthesis of melatonin, which can cause sleep difficulties, and raises homocysteine, which can damage arteries, increase plaque formation and boost the risk of cardiovascular disease.

Diuretics or "water pills," which, it seems, everybody takes, can deplete potassium. So-called "loop diuretics" such as furosemide can deplete calcium and magnesium. Calcium loss is significant for older women at risk of osteoporosis.

A substance called coenzyme Q10 has a cardioprotective effect and is vital to energy production inside the body. It is so important that a major manufacturer of cholesterol-lowering "statin" drugs is considering adding CoQ10 to these drugs, because they tend to deplete it. How many people taking these anti-cholesterol drugs know enough or are encouraged to supplement their diet with CoQ10? Very few. Wouldn't you say this is a wake-up call – something we should all be studying and acting on?

> A substance called coenzyme Q10 has a cardioprotective effect and is vital to energy production inside the body.

Many people take cardiovascular drugs, which include metoprolol, atenolol, pindolol, propranolol – to mention just a few – all of which have been identified as causing CoQ10 depletion. Potential depletion problems are seen in congestive heart failure, high blood pressure and low energy.

Then, too, many diseases can contribute to or worsen nutrient deficiencies. For example, diabetics don't use zinc very well, yet it's needed for wound healing. Diabetics may also be deficient in magnesium and chromium.

If you take anticonvulsants, you may experience nutrient depletion. For example, the drug Dilantin™ can deplete biotin, calcium, folic acid, vitamin B1, vitamin B12, vitamin D and vitamin K. Other anticonvulsant medications can cause similar losses. Anyone who takes medication on a regular basis should

> Anyone who takes medication on a regular basis should read the *Drug-Induced Nutrient Depletion Handbook* by Ross Pelton et al. It's listed in the Resources section.

read the *Drug-Induced Nutrient Depletion Handbook* by Ross Pelton et al. (It's listed in the Resources section.)

What I've mentioned here is just the tip of the iceberg. It's not my intention to give you a crash course on nutrition, but I do want you to be aware of how some prescription medications can adversely affect your health. If you want to Put Old on Hold, take responsibility – understand what medications can do for and to you. You just can't ignore the significance of this.

> If you want to Put Old on Hold, take responsibility – understand what medications can do for and to you.

What supplements are needed

Everything! Books, magazines, newsletters and the Internet abound with information about good nutrition and supplements. (If you need a push in the right direction, I've included some of my favorites in the Resources section.) I won't reinvent the wheel by summarizing a lot of information available in great depth from a variety of perspectives and from experts more qualified than I am. Rather, I want to present you with enough information about diet and supplements to stimulate your interest and motivate you to start educating yourself in earnest.

Before I get into specifics, I want to say something about buying supplements. Early on when vitamin supplements first started to appear on the market, a supplement was considered worthwhile only if it came from an "organic" source. Everything had to be "natural." My main source of nutrition information at that time was *Prevention* magazine when its founder, J. I. Rodale, was at the helm. He was really into organic farming so his recommendations favored organic products. For many years I tried to stay with organic or natural products, but as my education continued and broadened, I came to the conclusion other factors mattered as well. I've learned what's labeled "natural" or "organic" is not always necessary or better. I try to buy supplements from companies that have been in business a long time and are actively engaged in research. As you get on with your own education, you will learn to make good choices and decisions. The worst decision you can make is not to do anything at all for fear of making a wrong decision. If you are not taking supplements now and want to start, you can't go wrong if you purchase them from your pharmacy or a health food store with a good reputation.

> The worst decision you can make is not to do anything at all for fear of making a wrong decision.

There is so much you should know, I hardly know where to begin. But the following are several supplements that I believe are critical for Putting Old on Hold.

First on the list are antioxidants. Primary causes of aging are oxidants called free radicals, which result from the breakdown of what you ingest and from pollution. They are highly reactive and can attack healthy cells, weaken collagen and contribute to various diseases. As you age, your body becomes more vulnerable to the effects of free radicals.

Fortunately, you can supplement your diet with antioxidants that include vitamins C, E, CoQ10 and alpha lipoic acid. There are others, but these are my favorites. Remember, these are not recommendations – it's up to you to educate yourself about what's right for you.

Here are some cutting-edge findings that relate to the role of antioxidants in Putting Old on Hold:

- Alpha lipoic acid may be more potent than either ginkgo or vitamin E in protecting the brain. Because it's the only antioxidant that can easily get into the brain, it's considered useful in preventing damage from a stroke. It's been used for some time in Europe for supplementary treatment of diabetes and neurological diseases. One of alpha lipoic acid's amazing attributes is its ability to regenerate vitamins C and E after scavenging free radicals – enough to continue to fight still more free radicals.

- I love ginkgo – I take it every day and I believe it plays a major role in maintaining the integrity of my memory and cognitive ability. Ginkgo "networks" with vitamins C, E and alpha lipoic acid, providing a super-effective free radical fighting machine.

- CoQ10 is also enormously protective of the brain. CoQ10 recycles vitamin E. It also works with vitamin E in the skin, protecting against UV radiation. Research on this supplement is showing it is vitally important to maintain health and longevity in ways we can't imagine. Current thinking about CoQ10 is that the best comes from Japan.

- Networking antioxidants appear to be involved in preventing and combating gum disease. (Nearly half of Americans aged 65 to 74 have severe periodontal disease. Bacteria in the mouth associated with gum disease may be linked to heart disease, artery blockage and stroke.)

- People who take vitamin E are 40 to 50 percent less likely to die of cancer or heart disease; men who take vitamin E are also 42 percent less likely to die of prostate cancer.

- Antioxidants can keep cells youthful by preventing the accumulation of a waste product called lipofuscin. "Age spots" on the hands are one manifestation of lipofuscin.

- Antioxidants may be able to block activation of viral genes, keeping various viruses dormant.

- Polyphenols found in wine protect not only against heart disease, but also against certain cancers, Alzheimer's and macular degeneration. Moderate wine drinkers tend to live longer than teetotalers.

- While collagen is currently seen as a cure for wrinkles more so than a cure for the common cold, vitamin C's ability to stimulate collagen production and thus strengthen connective tissue is a vital part of the body's defense against viruses.

- Men can cut their risk of heart attack by 45 percent simply by taking 300 mg of vitamin C a day, according to a UCLA study.

- Antioxidants have a profound role in preventing cancer because they can switch on and off the genes that control cell growth.

The above information has been gleaned from a new book *The Antioxidant Miracle* by Lester Packer, director of the Packer Lab at the University of California, Berkeley. (It's listed in the Resources section of this book.)

Here's more useful information about vitamin C:

- Most people with diabetes have a greater than average need for vitamin C.

- Smoking depletes vitamin C.

- Long-term supplementation with vitamin C has been found to reduce the risk of developing cataracts.

- Vitamin C causes wounds to heal 40 to 50 percent faster than without it.

- Low vitamin C intake is a risk factor for asthma.

- Vitamin C is a natural antihistamine.

- High doses of vitamin C suppress the symptoms of HIV/AIDS and can significantly reduce the tendency for secondary infections.

Other supplements I like

- Soy and whey. I like them for their protein value because I don't eat a lot of meat – red or white.

- Glucosamine and chondroitin in conjunction with MSM (methylsulfonylmethane) for relief of joint pain. When these supplements work, and they often do so with dramatic results, they surely beat ibuprofen and other prescription anti-inflammatory drugs that have a lot of nasty side effects.

One day one of my customers asked if I noticed anything different about him. He was not using his cane. He was taking glucosamine, chondroitin and MSM. Miraculously, the combination relieved his joint pain to the extent he could even go dancing. He was happy beyond belief. He'd been given back his life. This is the stuff of which exaggerated TV commercials are made, but here was a real-life demonstration that a relatively simple, non-traditional approach to alleviating pain actually works. Not everyone is helped by this combination, but when it does work, it's amazing.

- Calcium, magnesium, folic acid, bioflavonoids, the entire B complex family.

- SAM-e, short for S-adenosylmethionine. It's a naturally occurring compound good for so many things and I take it as a preventive measure. It's been used to treat Parkinson's disease, multiple sclerosis and migraine headaches. It has been shown to stimulate cartilage growth and may reverse the underlying causes of osteoarthritis. Clinical trials have demonstrated SAM-e to have analgesic and anti-inflammatory effects. It has been compared to non-steroidal anti-inflammatories such as ibuprofen and naproxen without the side effects.

- Indole-3-carbinol. Based on studies I've seen, it shows great promise of protecting against breast cancer. My doctor, who practices integrative medicine, is very keen on this supplement.

- Bran & psyllium. Fiber plays a vital role in the ability to Put Old on Hold. A clean gut will go a long way toward preventing or alleviating a lot of health problems. It's been said death starts in chronically clogged intestines. Believe it!

- A "greens" supplement that is a freeze-dried mixture of green veggies, grasses and other good things. I don't think people get enough green stuff in their diets.

Water

And now we come to something really near and dear to my heart: *water*. Do you like water? If not, why not? Do you think you drink an adequate amount of water every day? What is adequate? A friend of mine carries around a pint bottle of water and sips it occasionally. She is convinced she drinks enough water. I don't think so.

> ... many problems traditionally associated with "old age" are not the result of the aging process, but the result of dehydration.

I personally believe many problems traditionally associated with "old age" are not the result of the aging process, but the result of dehydration. When counseling customers about their medication, I routinely ask how much water they consume. More times than not I'm told, "I don't like water. It makes me nauseous."

I recall most vividly an old woman complaining her saliva was so thick and she had sores in her mouth. I asked how much water she drank and predictably she said, "I don't drink water. It makes me sick to my stomach." No amount of scolding would have encouraged her to drink more water. Sadly, she was drying up from the inside out. She was in a process of what I call "near-death mummification." Unfortunately, I see a lot of it.

How much water is enough?

If you are sedentary and spend a lot of time in air-conditioned rooms, you will need less water than if you are outside working hard and sweating. I personally try to consume at least a half gallon a day, which is not a lot. Another rule of thumb is half an ounce of water per pound of body weight. And by the way, I don't drink tap water. I simply don't trust if for purity.

While some water contaminants result from natural sources such as pathogens from wildlife and toxic minerals that leach from ground minerals, my greatest concern is sewage, industrial waste, pesticide runoff, illegal dumping and just plain defective or ineffective treatment. I don't think there is a purification system in any municipality that is trustworthy. In 1993, Milwaukee, Wisconsin, experienced a disastrous outbreak of a gastrointestinal disease resulting from a pathogen called *cryptosporidium* in the water supply. As I recall, a very large number of people became sick, many were hospitalized and there were even deaths. In 1995, a study conducted by the Natural Resources Defense Council declared some 25,000 public water systems failed to meet EPA standards. That means millions of Americans did not, and probably still do not, drink water treated to remove lead, parasites and bacteria, to mention just a few deadly contaminants. These and other revealing reports have been a real wake-up call, motivating me to step up my resolve to avoid tap water whenever possible.

The other thing about tap water that concerns me is added chlorine and fluoride. I can accept chlorine in the water because it's necessary for purification. However, that's not an endorsement of chlorine. Chlorine reacts with naturally occurring organic matter, resulting in the formation of trihalomethanes (THMs), known to cause rectal and bladder cancers and birth defects.

I know all the arguments in favor of fluoridated water, but I don't buy them. Adding a toxic substance to a community's water supply, regardless of noble intent, doesn't make sense to me.

Exposure to fluoride occurs in so many ways – in toothpaste, mouthwash, chewing gum, vitamins and other sources of which you are unaware. How much is too much? How do you know how much you are swallowing from so many different sources? I don't know of any study that proves fluoride does not accumulate in the body and do irreparable harm. Do not be misled about fluoride – it is not a benign substance. Sodium fluoride is a strong poison and is great for killing roaches. However valuable minuscule amounts may be for preventing cavities in the teeth of children or osteoporosis in older people, I

> Do not be misled about fluoride – it is not a benign substance. Sodium fluoride is a strong poison and is great for killing roaches.

don't think it's wise for human use. I often wonder if exposure to excessive fluoride plays a role in the development of Alzheimer's or other common degenerative diseases.

What kind of water should you drink? I prefer bottled spring water. Anything labeled "purified" or just "drinking" water doesn't cut it for me. I am aware some expensive brands of bottled water have been found to contain unacceptable levels of bacteria. It's a chance you take no matter what brand you buy. I still think bottled water is better than tap water, particularly if your city is delivering sanitized waste water, as had been suggested and rejected (I hope forever) in my area.

What about gadgets you attach to your faucet? They improve the taste but probably don't get rid of fluoride, pesticides, bacteria and poisons such as lead, mercury or arsenic. Lead-based paints have been banned but drinking water still is fed through lead pipes. It is estimated that over half of the cities in the United States have lead or lead-lined pipes in municipal systems.

If you are determined to use tap water, at least have it tested by a private laboratory. In addition to knowing what's in the water sample you submit at the time, it will also give an indication of whether or not your house plumbing is adding anything dangerous to your water supply.

As well as bottled spring water, I also buy water called Penta-Hydrate Super Pro from Bio Hydration Research Labs in San Diego. This company turns ordinary water into something special by rearranging the molecular structure so it gets into your cells faster. It's fascinating and I wish I could explain the chemistry to you in a few simple sentences but I can't. But I can tell you this. It's great. My husband swears it helps relieve the pain in his knee. (Contact information for this special water is in the Resources section.)

Benefits of water

I truly believe water "rules" as nature's wonder drug. Here are some of the benefits you will derive from adequate water consumption:

- **It's a natural appetite suppressant.** Cold water seems to work best for this purpose. Try it when you feel hungry, particularly if you ate just a short while ago. Hunger is often a manifestation of hidden thirst. A woman asked me about the effectiveness of supplements to lose weight. Nothing she tried worked. When she said she was always hungry, I asked how much water she drank. "Hardly ever. It's overrated," she snapped. When I told her hunger was often a sign of hidden thirst, she grinned, narrowed her eyes and smirked, "Yeah, right."

- **Water helps the body burn stored fat.** When water intake is inadequate, fat deposits increase. This is because, without enough water, the kidneys don't function properly. They don't work up to capacity. When they don't work to capacity, the liver has to take over some of the load. One of the liver's duties is to burn stored fat. If the liver is overloaded with work the kidneys should be doing, it burns less fat and consequently more fat remains stored in the body.

- **Adequate water consumption is a great treatment for water retention.** When the body doesn't get enough water, it feels endangered and holds on to as much water as it can. This shows up as swollen ankles, legs and hands. Prescription diuretics offer a temporary solution, forcing out stored water and taking essential nutrients as well. As a result, the body senses a threat to survival and will replace the lost water as quickly as possible. The water retention then starts all over again. The best way to avoid the problem of water retention is to give your body plenty of water. Only then will stored water be released. It also helps to avoid excess salt. The more salt you consume, the more water your body needs to dilute it. Fortunately, it's easy to get rid of excess salt – just drink more water.

- Since **water is the key to fat metabolism,** if you are overweight you need more water than a thin person.

- **Water helps maintain muscle tone** by giving muscles their natural ability to contract and by preventing dehydration. Adequate water also helps prevent sagging skin after weight loss.

Be kind to your body; give it the water it wants and needs to function optimally. It will reward you by helping you to stay a juicy plum instead of becoming a dried up prune. If you have a medical problem, consult your physician before changing your water intake.

> Be kind to your body; give it the water it wants and needs to function optimally.

Can water "cure?"

F. Batmanghelidj, M.D., explains the role of water in alleviating problems commonly treated with medications in *Your Body's Many Cries for Water.* He maintains water is useful to treat just about everything from arthritis to depression, and whether it's true or not, I don't know. But he does present some intriguing ideas and testimonials from those "cured" with water.

For example, he maintains heartburn pain indicates a state of dehydration and relates how he successfully treated a patient with this problem – just with water. A young man was suffering with agonizing stomach pain. He had taken several cimetidine tablets and a whole bottle of antacid without relief. (Believe it or not, it's not uncommon for those in search of relief for a stomach problem to consume an entire bottle of antacid on a regular basis. That is *real* health abuse!) After determining the patient didn't have a perforated ulcer, the doctor had him drink a total of three glasses of water, which resulted in complete remission of pain in a short period of time. I personally have heard testimonies about the effectiveness of water in treating stomach pain, but unless you experience it yourself, it could be difficult to believe. After all, water is just water, isn't it?

At work one evening, a young woman appeared at the prescription counter with a prescription for ranitidine, commonly used to treat heartburn. I asked her how much water she drinks and she replied, "As little as possible. Water makes me sick." I thought, well, maybe Dr. Batmanghelidj knows what he is talking about. I told her about his book but it fell on deaf ears. She didn't like water and that was that. Anyway, how could something as simple as water stop stomach pain? A closed mind is a terrible thing.

(I have listed *Your Body's Many Cries for Water* in the Resources section. Although it sometimes tends to be technical, nevertheless, enough is in plain English and will give you a lot of food for thought.)

To recap, here are the benefits you can expect from optimum intake of water:

- You will look and feel better.

- Fluid retention is alleviated as stored water is eliminated.

- The liver is free to burn stored fat and stored fat is burned.

- Natural thirst returns.

- If you are trying to lose weight, there is loss of hunger almost immediately.

Medications

At the beginning, I said I held unconventional and controversial views. (That should be evident by now!) Here's one of them: You can't Put Old on Hold if you take a lot of unnecessary medication.

That's a strong statement, but bear with me as I explain what I mean. Remember, I am speaking from my experience and you may not agree with the way I see things. I respect your right to disagree, and ask you to have an open mind about my point of view.

From my perspective, there are two types of medication: (1) Those needed for conditions such as seizures or infections or some problem that can't be controlled or managed except with medication, and (2) Medications taken to control or alleviate symptoms caused by poor lifestyle choices. For example, drugs taken for "heartburn," "dyspepsia," "GERD," "acid reflux,"– problems I believe are often diet related. Unnecessary use and abuse of medication to remedy lifestyle-induced problems results, at least in part, from prevailing thought that says it's okay to abuse your body because you can overcome the abuse by swallowing a pill.

Here's a perfect example of "approved" abuse: A TV ad for an antacid product depicts a race car driver who must have something to eat after each lap around the track. After the first lap, he eats greasy ribs. After the second lap, he eats greasy fries.

Third lap? Advertised antacid to the rescue! Fourth lap? He's apparently the winner of the race so there is a huge cake and, yes, more antacid to take care of the cake. Does this way of eating make sense to you?

> Poor health is not due to aging.

Poor health is not due to aging. Barring inherited conditions, you stay in good health not by dependence on medication but by aggressively taking care of yourself. Remember Dr. Rowe's 70-30 ratio. Lifestyle choices matter!

Today's drugs are like nothing in the past

Fifty years ago, my father's drug store was a naturalist's delight. Bottles and packages of pharmaceutical-grade roots, leaves, stems, bark, flowers and berries of plants lined the shelves. My father used them to make tinctures, syrups, elixirs and concoctions of every description to treat everything from syphilis to sore throat. I remember one of the sore throat remedies he made and sold as "Iron Mixture." It was the most vile-tasting stuff you could possibly imagine, but it worked. Were some of those botanicals harmful if used improperly? Of course, but doctors and pharmacists knew how and when and in what form to use them wisely.

Then, as now, "nervousness" was a common complaint and Elixir of Phenobarbital was the drug of choice to soothe the symptoms. Also then as now, stomach and intestinal complaints were common and a mixture compounded of three or four herbal ingredients made life bearable. A prescription probably cost a customer $1.50 for a month's supply. Whatever did people do without today's high-tech, obscenely expensive antidepressants and proton pump inhibitors? (The latter is a type of stomach medication, not a machine.) There was just as much if not more to be depressed about (like World War II), but people learned how to cope without medicinal crutches. It wasn't until the appearance of penicillin, followed soon after by more powerful antibiotics, that medication usage began to change. For example, pre-penicillin, when kids got sick with a cold, it just had to run its course with the help of simple remedies to alleviate aches and fever. It didn't take long for that to change once doctors started prescribing penicillin to avoid possible "secondary infections" when a child had a simple cold.

In retrospect, yesterday's drugs (before penicillin) were relatively benign compared to today's medications, which are highly complex, laboratory-engineered substances, targeted for specific ailments and often displaying bizarre and unexpected side effects.

For example, a medication called cimetidine, used to treat stomach problems, also eliminates plantar warts on the bottom of the feet. I was totally unaware of this "side effect" until a customer handed me a prescription for cimetidine, written by a podiatrist. I immediately thought the doctor was prescribing out of his area of expertise, and I actually got a little huffy about it. I was ready to call and read him the riot act but decided to talk to the customer first. The story is that the podiatrist had discovered cimetidine is useful to treat plantar warts. Think about that. A medication created to target a specific area of the body (stomach) can affect another area of the body in a totally unexpected way. It scares me. Are there other "sleeper" side effects of this or similar drugs now sold over the counter and available to anyone?

> Do you pay attention to the side effects rattled off during TV commercials for prescription drugs?

Do you pay attention to the side effects rattled off during TV commercials for prescription drugs? You should – it's an education. Watch the "direct to consumer" (DTC) advertising of prescription products. For example, one advertisement says medication designed to alleviate arthritis may cause sudden, unexpected internal bleeding, or liver or kidney damage. Another type of advertised medication is declared to possibly cause flu or ear infections or some other bizarre side effect. Is anyone listening? How can medicine cause flu or an ear infection? Flu is caused by a virus and infection is caused by bacteria. The commercials are so cleverly done that what remains in the viewer's mind is not the litany of possible horrendous side effects but the beautiful colorful visual effects, the music, the happiness, the promise of relief. The commercials are very effective – they sell an enormous amount of medication.

Problems with multiple medications

Experiencing severe or disturbing side effects from taking multiple medications is another problem.

This is what happens. You take medication A for arthritis. While alleviating some pain, it causes stomach and intestinal problems. So your doctor prescribes medication B to offset the side effects of medication A.

In turn, medication B has side effects of its own. It may cause drowsiness or nausea. You tell the doctor about these side effects and he prescribes medication C to control them. In turn, medication C may create yet other problems.

So before you know it, you may be taking three or more medications. And you wonder why you don't feel well.

Yes, medication is necessary to control diabetes and runaway blood pressure. It helps lower nasty cholesterol, but diet and lifestyle changes may help as much or more.

Yes, medication is necessary to control pain, infection, seizures, or some condition you were born with or acquired.

There are all kinds of legitimate uses for medication and we'd be lost without the relief they provide. All medication is not bad. It's the overuse, misuse and abuse

> All medication is not bad. It's the overuse, misuse and abuse that's bad.

that's bad. Most medications taken over a period of time are extremely hard on vital organs such as the liver and kidneys. Prolonged medication use, necessary or not, will seriously impair your ability to Put Old on Hold. Your goal should be to acquire optimum health so, if possible, you won't need a chemical crutch to get you through each day of your life.

A smart way to Put Old on Hold

Putting Old on Hold doesn't start when you reach a particular chronological milestone. It begins *right now*, whatever your age. One of the smartest tools you can use to Put Old on Hold is a comprehensive blood test called the CBC/Chemistry Profile. It's relatively inexpensive and measures 35 blood factors that can have a significant impact on your health. Unfortunately, HMOs trying to save money are not suggesting CBC/ Chemistry Profiles that would help

> One of the smartest tools you can use to Put Old on Hold is a comprehensive blood test called the CBC/Chemistry Profile.

detect a lot of problems before they gain a toehold. Even though the Federal Drug Administration (FDA) mandates regular blood testing if you are taking certain medications, doctors often do not prescribe blood tests. So the bottom line is, it's up to you so make sure you get tested. And not just once in your lifetime, but every year. If your doctor won't order a test, or if your insurance won't pay, bite the financial bullet and make arrangements on your own. Remember, your health is *your* responsibility. One way you can arrange for testing is through the Life Extension Nutrition Center. You can place an order for a CBC/Chemistry Profile and other tests by calling 800-208-3444.

Why is a CBC/Chemistry Profile important? For several reasons:

- Detection of calcium imbalance. If too much calcium leaches from bone and is deposited in the vascular system, you may not know it until you suffer a fracture, kidney stone or heart valve failure due to calcification. If calcium imbalance is caught early enough, it can be corrected with dietary changes before it becomes a full-blown problem. The CBC/Chemistry Profile can be a lifesaver in this case.

- Detection of high serum glucose, which accelerates development of arterial and neurological conditions. If found in time, lifestyle changes including better nutrition can be a lifesaver.

- Detection of excessive amounts of iron, which rampantly generates free radicals that increase the risk of cancer, Alzheimer's and Parkinson's disease.

- Aging results in major changes in hormone balance. In both men and women, failure to correct this imbalance can play a role in cardiovascular disease, some types of cancer, Type II diabetes, osteoporosis, depression, abdominal obesity and reduced physical and mental energy levels. Typically, most doctors, when treating a woman for menopause, will not do a blood test to determine exactly how much or how little hormone replacement is needed, but will go ahead and prescribe Premarin™ or another synthetic hormone replacement. If that's what has happened to you, insist on a blood test or get one on your own. It's your body and your life and you have a right to know if you are being treated appropriately.

- But perhaps the most important reason to have a CBC/Chemistry Profile is to check on how well your liver and kidneys are doing if you are taking on-going prescription medication. Older people take a lot of medication on a regular basis, and I'm not talking just about those in their sixties and beyond. Boomers take their share of daily drugs, and taking regular doses of medication is trending down to ever-younger ages. Adverse reactions to prescription medication contribute to the demise of some 200,000 people year. That shouldn't happen. If tested in a timely manner, drug-induced liver and kidney damage could be uncovered before it results in disability or death.

The liver and kidneys are under constant assault, not just from medication but also from all kinds of toxic substances in the environment and especially from chemical-laden products ingested as "food." I am convinced these two vital organs were never designed to process the wide range of complex and toxic chemicals that assault them on a daily basis. If you read labels and can't pronounce the names of chemical additives in food products you buy and eat every day, then just assume your liver and kidneys will have to work overtime to detoxify them. Constant stress on these organs eventually takes a toll. Clearly, between prescription medication and faulty diet choices, there is a clear need for annual blood testing. It's up to you to see that it gets done.

Insider information

Let me give some "insider" information about medications. I hope this will really get you thinking.

In the pharmacy, there are many categories of medications. Here are just a few:

Antibiotics	Cholesterol control
Contraceptives	Gastric disorder relief
Pain relief	Mood alteration
High blood pressure	Hormone replacement
Respiratory problems	

On this list, only one category of medication can produce a cure – the antibiotics. The rest just alleviate or manage symptoms. Think about that.

Could diet and lifestyle have a bearing, to some degree or another, on a lot of conditions represented in the above categories? Absolutely.

I see customers come to the prescription counter with shopping carts overflowing with the makings of their All American diet of manufactured, synthetic, pseudo food, heavy with grease, refined sugar, assorted chemicals, processed or "fresh" meat perhaps in an advanced state of putrefaction and bulging with diarrhea-inducing bacteria. Then they pick up prescriptions for high blood pressure, high cholesterol, gastric upset and arthritis pain. There is little doubt in my mind that with better diet and lifestyle choices, less medication would be needed.

Older people trapped in the cycle of food abuse and prescription drug relief may be living longer with the help of their medications, but often they are not living well. It is not uncommon to hear them complain, "I'm taking all this medication my doctor prescribed

> Older people trapped in the cycle of food abuse and prescription drug relief may be living longer with the help of their medications, but often they are not living well.

and I still don't feel well." These are "old" people in every sense of the word. They can't Put Old on Hold. The only thing they have "on hold" is a visit from the Grim Reaper, which might be welcomed by some hurting souls. I can't tell you the number of times I've heard, "I don't know why God is keeping me here."

One customer in particular comes to mind. She's about my age, and I refer to her as "the gray lady" because of the gray pallor of her skin and lack of expression on her face and in her eyes. She complains she doesn't feel well, but she doesn't need to tell me – it's obvious. Her speech and movement are slow and labored. She takes a lot of medication – her doctor appears to try anything and everything to make her feel better. She obediently gets her prescriptions filled every month and gets upset if her order is not ready on time. She is convinced she will die if she misses one dose of medicine. I personally think she is over-medicated and might feel better if she took less, but then, that's just my unconventional opinion.

Take care of your health early on because, clearly, health does not come out of a prescription bottle.

Retirement

Overview

It's a given: The face of "old age" is changing. People are living longer and staying in the workforce longer, so why pay too much attention to retirement? Between those who must continue to work for financial reasons and those who choose to stay productive because they want to, why discuss retirement at all?

While more people are choosing not to retire than ever before, most people want to retire and will do so if given the opportunity. With just minimal encouragement, it's human nature to want to kick back and do nothing, or do what gives the greatest amount of pleasure. Our society is leisure oriented. Work is a drag; fun is where it's at. Problem is, the human mind and body do not fare well when left to their inclination to choose inactivity.

> The human mind and body do not fare well when left to their inclination to choose inactivity.

Constant admonitions that at age 65 "it's time to stop and smell the roses," "you've worked hard all your life, now it's time to take it easy," "you've earned the right to do nothing" fuel the penchant for leisure. As early as 50, a relentless drumbeat of retirement sound bites emerge from every direction, suggesting life is about over. Reaching the mid-century mark legitimizes the barrage of negative advice addressing every possible need imaginable, from retirement planning to retirement housing.

It's not just a social phenomenon; it's a huge industry that's not going to go away. Make no mistake: Retirement is definitely a destination of choice for many because it's the traditional and "right" thing to do. So we need to talk about it here.

Why retire?

There are just two reasons to retire:

1. You simply don't want to work any more. You are tired of taking orders from some numbskull who isn't half as smart as you are. You want to be your own boss and finally do what you want to do and go where you want to go when you want to. After all, you've worked long and hard and you've earned your retirement. Custom says it's time. You are ready for the senior lifestyle. Your friends are doing it. You want to travel. You'd like to take a trip around the world. Or just crank up the RV and get on the road with your significant other, with whom you will love being cooped up around the clock.

   You are ready for Bingo games, early bird discount dinners at the best restaurants in town, hanging out at the senior center and playing cards or shuffleboard with like-minded peers. You'd like to go back to school, take some classes and learn to use a computer. In short, you just want your personal liberation from the daily grind and conformity, unaware you will soon be moving on to another type of conformity often found in the lifestyle of retired seniors.

2. The other reason to retire is because you don't have a choice. Your health may have given out and you are unable to continue to work. Or family obligations may require your full attention. Yes, there are legitimate reasons to retire, but darn few of them.

Retirement Realities

Okay, you understand your reasons to retire. Now let's look at some retirement realities.

Think about the meaning of the word "retirement." Really give it some thought. No, give it a *lot* of thought, because it's a very powerful word. Ernest Hemingway called it the most depressing word in the English Language and he was right. It can be devastating.

Think about what "retirement" really means beyond the golf, the travel, the gardening or whatever retirees are supposed to find so much fulfillment in doing. Acceptance and internalization of the word "retirement" as a state of being sets into motion a nonstop mental and physical meltdown. Your body starts to shut down because "retirement" tells the subconscious you are letting go of life. And your body does its best to help make it happen.

When you are not required to deal with what is outside of your comfort zone or wrestle with mental challenges on a daily basis, mental and physical decline are inevitable. You lose your edge. You begin to think, walk and talk more slowly. Your reaction time slows, and it's not necessarily the result of the aging process. That's the reality. Use it or lose it.

> Use it
> or
> lose it.

Our "throwaway" society doesn't value much of anything with a lot of mileage on it. We give it away, trade it in for something of lesser value, melt it down, bury it, burn it or let it rot. We pretend we're being practical when discarding or retiring "old stuff" even when it's in good working order or can still be put to use. Old battle ships, no longer considered useful but in perfect working order, are retired. Taken out to the middle of the ocean and sunk (talk about money down the drain), they become an expensive habitat for sea life and amusement for divers and treasure hunters. Similarly, the state of retirement sinks the human spirit and encourages decline and decay.

Retirement Reality No. 1:
Loss of income and decline in quality of life

This is a biggie. Financial gurus say you need 70 percent of your pre-retirement income to live well in retirement. For me, I can't imagine trying to live on less than our current income. Unexpected expenses can pop up at any time of life, but inevitably, they seem to cost a lot more and there are more of them when you are older. Of course you can cut back and do without, but that's not fun. It would be like starting all over again, if you can remember how things were financially when you first married or were trying to establish your career. Your prime time is not the time to be pinching pennies and depending on special senior perks to help meet expenses.

> Your prime time is not the time to be pinching pennies and depending on special senior perks to help meet expenses.

To understand the significance of having an adequate income, I wish you could be in my shoes and see seniors, as I do on a daily basis, relying on Social Security and little else. It's heartbreaking. Having $7 to cover the co-pay for your medication may not be a big deal when you have sufficient income, but it's tragic when you don't have it and won't have it until the end of the month when your paltry Social Security check arrives. Think about that – not having $7 in your pocket! If you think that's sad, think about the Social Security dependent senior who takes six or more medications each month, and some of them cost a lot more than $7 each. Many seniors on Social Security spend so much money on medication, they have little left over for food – and forget about buying supplements.

If you are to stay healthy, live reasonably well and Put Old on Hold, you will need money – a lot of it – not just for medication but also for quality food and costly maintenance that includes vitamins and food supplements. Sorry, I don't care what anybody says, this is not the time of life to even think about cutting back.

Is there a solution? Yes. Many seniors, in spite of health problems, are perfectly capable of working, and they should work as long as it is in keeping with their ability and preferences. It would get them back in touch with the real world and give a tremendous boost to their self worth, not to mention their quality of life. A financial penalty no longer exists for retirees on Social Security who want to work, so that excuse for inactivity is gone. It would be wonderful if government or private programs were available specifically to encourage and prepare healthy retirees – the older the better – to get back to earning a wage. Apparently, many retirees do want to work. The editor of *Senior Spotlight*, a local publication in my area, recently lamented, "Every time I have been told a Senior-Back-to-Work program would be set up, it falls apart . . . so many qualified seniors are looking for work." Funding is available for so many questionable programs – why is it so difficult to get assistance for a program that could radically improve the lives of many older people? It would solve a lot of financial, social and health problems. Poverty is the pits when there is an alternative, like having a job. (One

> Many seniors, in spite of health problems, are perfectly capable of working, and they should work, as long as it is in keeping with their ability and preferences.

Senior-Back-to-Work Program can be reached at 1506 Oak Drive # 73, Vista, CA 92084.)

Finding rewarding jobs for seniors may be easier in the near future, at least in California. A report by University of California's California Policy Research Center will be used by the state Health and Human Services Agency to develop a plan as early as 2003 to handle the increase in residents over age 65. Recommendations include offering tax credits to employers who hire and retrain seniors, and it won't happen a moment too soon. It is projected that by 2020, California will have 6.5 million seniors aged 65 or older – compared to 3.5 million in 2001-2002.

Retirement Reality No. 2:
Problems re-entering the workforce

If you retire for even a brief period of time, then decide retirement isn't for you and want to go back to your former line of work, it may be difficult if you haven't kept your skills current. It doesn't take long to get stale and lose your mental and physical edge. I have seen this happen with pharmacists who can't wait to get out of the business. The long hours and stress of dealing with the public eventually take a toll. After six months or a year away from the daily grind, they decide they are bored or need money and go back to work. Yet the person who retired six months or a year ago is no longer the same person. Mental and physical agility have become impaired. They think, speak, move, react and learn more slowly. There is a definite difference. They've simply lost their edge and the sad thing is, the edge is sometimes difficult to resurrect. Not

> If you retire for even a brief period of time, then decide retirement isn't for you and want to go back to your former line of work, it may be difficult if you haven't kept your skills current.

impossible, but difficult. Some pharmacists, recognizing their retirement-induced deficiencies, give up and retreat into inactivity. It's a great loss of ability and knowledge.

I suggest staying employed as long as possible. Keep up your skills. The bridge from the real world to retirement is short, alluring and convenient. If you retire and decide to take the road back, you may find it rocky at best or impassable at worst. Of course, if you are lucky, you may reach a fork in the road that will lead you to a new and exciting place. But that usually only happens in the movies.

> Stay employed as long as possible. Keep up your skills.

Does this mean you should never take a vacation from work? Not at all. It's important to give your mind, body and spirit the opportunity to rest and rejuvenate. Periodically you need time away from everyday concerns to think, let go of unproductive stress, and allow your brain to process your budding ideas and clarify goals. Just be certain you understand the difference between a vacation and a "slide into retirement." You are on vacation when you know you are returning to something fulfilling, challenging and productive – something you eagerly look forward to tackling.

Sliding into retirement is deceptively easy. Retirement happens two ways – deliberately or inadvertently. The latter occurs when you tell yourself you are just enjoying an extended vacation – taking time to stop and smell the roses. You revel in the intoxicating scent of freedom and inhale so deeply of its sweetness that you drift into a state of mindless inebriation. Before you know where time went, you are no longer smelling the roses; you are pushing up daisies. On your tombstone the following words are etched: "Mary Jones: She stopped so long to smell the roses, she neglected to pursue her dreams and reach her potential. Her greatness is interred here with her remains."

Rest and restore yourself, then get on with living. Fulfill your dreams and develop your innate gifts. It's an exciting adventure too good to forfeit just because of chronological age.

Retirement Reality No. 3:
Loss of self esteem and personal power

Many seniors suffer from depression. It is my opinion depression often results from a loss or traumatic event in your life. That's not the only cause, of course, but a significant cause. Retirement, no matter how much you may look forward to it, is a major and traumatic event. It's closure on a lifetime of effort. It's saying goodbye to a part of you that will never exist again, except in memory.

> Retirement, no matter how much you may look forward to it, is a major and traumatic event.

Today you are a doctor, lawyer or accountant. Tomorrow you retire and become a "retired doctor," a "retired lawyer," a "retired accountant." The valued "somebody" is suddenly a retired, less-than-adequate "nobody." How often have you heard it said of someone, "Didn't he used to be a lawyer?" Sure, he lost his brains and ability because he retired? Of course not, but that's the unstated assumption. You wouldn't want a retired surgeon to operate on you – after all, his skills must have become rusty – or have they? You wouldn't want a retired lawyer to defend you in court – after all, he's retired and must not be as sharp as he used to be – or is he? You wouldn't want a retired accountant to prepare your tax return – after all, he probably hasn't kept up on changes in the law – or has he? Doesn't matter – they are all retired and, like it or not, the little black cloud of "retirement incompetence" will hover over them wherever they go. It will shape the way they see themselves and are seen in the world.

Some time ago I had a conversation with an 81-year-old man who works as an investment consultant for a firm in San Diego. He was really interesting for a couple of reasons. First, in speaking to him on the phone (I've never met him personally), I would never have guessed his age. His voice was strong and youthfully masculine, and he expressed himself quickly and clearly.

His views on the downside of retirement confirmed my thinking. He felt retirement could be particularly difficult for a man who, pre-retirement, held a managerial or other powerful position. One day he is behind a desk giving orders and treated with deference and respect. The day after he retires, it's all over.

A lifetime of finding identity in his work is gone. Forever. If he is married, he is now taking orders from a new boss – a wife who likely has been in charge of the home and has seniority in domestic management decisions. She has her daytime lifestyle and he had his, and now, it's her lifestyle, like it or not. If he gets bored, he can accompany his wife on shopping trips to the supermarket and drive her crazy telling her what to buy or not buy. That she has successfully planned meals without his help for the past umpteen years and doesn't need his help now never occurs to him. Or maybe he can tag along when she has a yen to cruise around the mall and he can cool his heels while she tries on clothing in one department store after another. We've all seen the old guys at malls, huddled together on benches, looking dour and impatient while the wives and their girlfriends shop till they drop. Or maybe he can have fun sitting in on his wife's bridge games, dishing the dirt with the girls. No kidding – retirement can result in major friction in a marriage previously considered harmonious by both partners.

It cannot be argued: After you retire, your value as a human being and your professional or business abilities are diminished in the eyes of the world. When it happens to you and you know you are still the same capable person, the negative feedback does terrible things to your self-esteem.

Is that frightening? You bet it is. The subconscious understands the word "retirement" means closing the door on life. In the state of retirement, focused on the past and without life-affirming goals for the future, you live with that reality. Each day gets closer to the inevitable and that's enough to make anyone feel depressed.

At this point, I'd like to say something about volunteerism for seniors as it relates to "staying busy" and maintaining one's self-esteem.

Many worthwhile causes and institutions could not function without unpaid help, so volunteer work is vital. For young people in particular, volunteer work is even wonderful. It teaches about life, the benefits and virtues of giving to others and expecting no money in return. It helps them understand the significance and necessity of sacrifice. As a bonus for young people, volunteer work can open doors to new and challenging business and career opportunities. It's a perfect win-win situation when the door swings both ways.

> Many worthwhile causes and institutions could not function without unpaid help, so volunteer work is vital ... [but] I have mixed feelings about seniors working gratis unless they have an income that allows them to live above the poverty level.

However, I don't encourage volunteer work as a preferred retirement activity because, frankly, I have mixed feelings about seniors working gratis unless they have an income that allows them to live above the poverty level. If they are struggling financially, as too many are, and are capable of productive work, they should have a paying job.

I have a friend who does volunteer work several days a week. She's only marginally "okay" financially so I asked why she volunteers instead of having a paying job. She said she would like extra income but "because of her age," she doesn't feel totally competent to hold a paying job. As a volunteer she feels she works on her terms, which is not entirely true – they wouldn't keep her on and rely on her as they do if she didn't "produce." Because she's been doing the same volunteer work for years, she's as competent as one could ask. How sad she has so little faith in her ability "because of her age."

For an individual at any age and in any circumstances, it warms the heart and soul to freely choose to help others. Such kindness should be encouraged. Yet, there is magic in receiving a paycheck for work well done. It is liberating both financially and emotionally; it boosts self-esteem as little else can, particularly at a time in life when self-sufficiency is not expected or encouraged.

Retirement Reality No. 4:
Adopting the senior lifestyle

Without question, opportunities to expand your world come with retirement – if you are healthy enough to travel or go back to school and can afford the expense. For many, this is a happy and fulfilling way of life. They are "staying active" and engaged, but not particularly productive or challenged. All that is okay – whatever "floats their boat."

In my experience, many retirees (certainly not all) live in a narrow, sheltered world in which they see the same people every day. They stay close to home, venturing out to go shopping, to the doctor's or to church. There is little if any challenge to keep their intellect fired up and alert. They sit passively in front of a TV most of the day, unaware the brain and body are turning to mush. They find it difficult to keep up with change. I recall a retired woman on anti-depressant medication complaining the world was moving so fast, and she couldn't keep up with everything – particularly computers – and it made her feel left behind. It bothered her terribly. Don't allow yourself to get to such a state. Welcome change and embrace it. A good

> Welcome change and embrace it. A good way to do it is to stay in touch with young people.

way to do it is to stay in touch with young people. They thrive on change and you can emulate the best coping techniques that work for them. It will help you Put Old on Hold.

Another aspect of the senior lifestyle is the resurgence of the "group mentality" phenomenon.

Just as teens associate in "packs" to establish their identity, define their lifestyle and find emotional support, many seniors become similarly group dependent. They refer to themselves as "us old people" and take a perverse pride in inviting pity, playing up feebleness, using deprecating terms to describe their age, circumstances or abilities. Personal identity and independence are lost to group decisions and activities. This observation certainly does not apply to all "old people," but I see enough of it on a daily basis to view it with alarm.

There is often the development of an irrational "group entitlement" mentality. For example, at the onset of flu season in the fall of 2000, it soon became evident flu vaccine was in short supply and scheduled shots had to be canceled. Most people accepted the situation, but one woman was irate. "But

I'm a senior citizen," she wailed, childishly. "We're supposed to get them before anybody else." Be on guard for unreasonable self-absorption. Whiney, complaining "victims" cannot and do not Put Old on Hold. Clearly, not all old people exhibit this type of behavior, but enough of them do to call for monitoring your mindset as you age.

And speaking of narrowing your world and regressing to teenage group-dependent behavior, observe the retirement community phenomenon – the ultimate resurgence of the teen group mentality.

Most people living in retirement communities are happy and content. They wouldn't live any place else and that's fine, but I think it's an unnatural environment in which to live. Featuring gates, guards, walls, security cameras, perfectly mani-cured rolling lawns, topiary, sculptures, waterfalls and ponds complete with ethereal white swans, retirement communities often seem like a cross between a minimum security prison and a cemetery. I have friends who moved into a retirement community believing it would be utopian. They quickly dis-covered it wasn't for them. Of course, these friends were independent types and should have realized that lifestyle was not for them. But then, they weren't expecting regimentation – just a nice life.

Take for example, my friend Mitzy.

Mitzy was married to an actor. He struggled for a long time and Mitzy, dutiful wife that she was, put up with him and supported him until he finally landed a role in a successful TV sit-com. Their new prosperity was a mixed blessing. Mr. Star fell in love with a younger woman right after he and Mitzy bought a newer and bigger house. A divorce followed soon after that. Mitzy got the house plus a financial settlement and life was good until the money was no longer sufficient to keep her in the style to which she had become accustomed. So she sold the house and moved into a lovely retirement community. It had every amenity you could imagine. Residents just needed to be 50 years old or older and Mitzy barely qualified.

After a couple of years, we lost touch. Then one day she called to tell me she was leaving "Heavenly Hills." She finally realized she wasn't living life the way she really wanted to live it. Mitzy loves to ice skate and during the time she was in Paradise, she didn't skate once. That was because this elegant enclave surrounded by the requisite walls, gates, guards and security cameras had an activities director ("the warden") who made sure everybody did the same thing every week. It was wonderful because everybody really got to know each other and bond as a community. (The teenage group-dependent phenomenon?) The women purchased their clothes at the pricey boutique on the grounds and soon they all began to look alike. They all ate the same food in the elegant community dining room. They visited each other when sick or in the hospital and grieved when "one of their own" was summoned by the Grim Reaper, which was rather frequent. She got tired of the old geezers, flirting with senility, trying to hit on her. Sometimes they'd start to make a pass, then forget what they were about and fumbled, dropping the ball, so to speak. While she was annoyed with the old guys, she was definitely interested in finding a significant other. Mitzy missed interacting with young people. She is a great looking gal and likes younger guys like her former husband, Mr. Star, now divorced from his Baby Doll.

She began to feel like a programmed robot. She wanted to get out and ice skate again. The day she called me, she asked if I would go with her. Would I? You bet. I hadn't been skating in a

> Independent people thrive best when they stay in an open environment, in constant contact with all kinds of people of all ages, free to come and go and make their own decisions about how to live.

long time either, and we could hold each other up and, maybe, Mitzy could meet some cute young guys.

There is a lesson to be learned here – a lesson not for everyone, of course. The lesson is that independent people thrive best when they stay in an open environment, in constant contact with all kinds of people of all ages, free to come and go and make their own decisions about how to live. The real world may be stressful at times, but it is the *real* world.

Retirement Reality No. 5: Unproductive use of time

> "Most people, when they are left free to fill their own time according to their own choice, are at a loss to think of anything sufficiently pleasant to be worth doing."

Philosopher and mathematician Bertrand Russell observed the importance of work in his book, *The Conquest of Happiness*. In it he states, "Most people, when they are left free to fill their own time according to their own choice, are at a loss to think of anything sufficiently pleasant to be worth doing . . . To be able to fill leisure intelligently is the last product of civilization, and at present, very few people have reached this level.[1]"

I witness this truth every day. It's not people working hard and trying to make ends meet that are usually miserable. It's those with so much time on their hands that they can focus on minor annoyances and minor troubles in their lives. For many retirees, still capable of mental and physical productivity, and

---

1 *The Conquest of Happiness*, Chapter 14 page 162

needing "something" to prove to themselves and others their existence has meaning, create problems or situations for which they provide or try to provide solutions.

Example: Because so many seniors are in dire straights financially, they spend a lot of time trying to figure out how to get the most for their money. Which is good, but in the process they can take a lot of your time, asking questions you can't answer such as why your price is $2.00 higher than a competitor. A retiree recently accosted me with that question. I told him I didn't know why our price was $2.00 higher – it was a corporate decision and prices are computer generated. He didn't seem to understand what I was talking about so he persisted, "Well, why don't you know? It's your job to know." What is one to say in response? I gave him an 800 number to call for a more satisfactory answer. Apparently the 800 number didn't work out because he was back the next day, asking for a specific name and address to which he could direct his question. And why not – "It's the people with so much time on their hands that they can focus on minor annoyances and minor troubles in their lives." Perhaps creating a problem for himself and solving it made him feel useful and productive.

Here's another example: We were living in an enclave of townhouses originally built for occupants 18 and older. There were no walls, no gates, no guards – it was a restricted development in one section of town. The community regulations were very strict and included the requirement that pet owners must clean up after their pets. At the time, we had a little cockapoodle that weighed about 10 pounds dripping wet. Being conscientious pet owners and good neighbors, when we walked our little darling, we always carried a bag and scooper and did our part to keep the community in the required pristine condition.

I recall three distinct incidents that gave credence to Bertrand Russell's observation about having too much time to fuss about minor annoyances.

On one occasion, our little precious stopped to leave a little pile on someone's lawn and we dutifully picked it up. As we were walking away, an elderly man opened a window and yelled, "Stop that! It leaves a terrible smell behind!" What were we to do? We had completely cleaned up the mess. We decided that on future outings we would carry a can of disinfectant spray and spritz the offending area after picking up. After all, we wanted to be good neighbors.

Another time our little darling took a particularly long time to urinate. When she finally decided she was done and we started to walk away, a woman flung open her door and screamed, "Go back and pick it up!" Well, there was nothing to pick up. It had already seeped into the ground.

Yet another time, as we were walking past a neighbor, our little dear stopped to leave a few drops. The neighbor whom we had greeted with a cheery "hello" glared at us and snarled, "Your dog is staining the grass!"

I relate these stories to encourage you to monitor your thinking, behavior and emotional state closely as the years roll by. Now, while you still have your wits about you, resolve to constantly stay aware of your conduct and mental outlook, and notice how it may be changing over time. As a reality check, evaluate how your "social performance" stacks up against that of young people. The purpose is to emulate not their immaturity but their spontaneity and ability to stay flexible. Your behavior will take care of itself if you continue to remain in the real world, physically, mentally and emotionally. It will help you maintain your self-respect and sensitivity to the feelings of others. It will definitely help you Put Old on Hold.

I can immediately tell a totally retired senior and one who is still working, even part-time. The difference is like day and night. The person still involved with the realities of life is much more reasonable and easier to deal with. That person is Putting Old on Hold.

Having made some negative comments and observations about retirement and retirees, I acknowledge many retired people are happy with their lifestyle. They are totally content; they consider their lives full and even overflowing with activity. There aren't enough hours in the day to do what they want to do – shopping, taking care of the home, cooking, taking classes, gardening, vacations, golf, doctor's visits.

Those blissful people are entitled to do what they want to do and no one would take any of their happiness away from them. They find comfort and satisfaction in the sameness of a day-to-day routine. Happiness, like beauty, is in the eye and experience of the beholder.

As I see it, those happy folks are not Putting Old on Hold because Putting Old on Hold is beyond their comprehension or interest. They see themselves as old people and that's the way they define themselves. They are going with the flow, doing what they believe they should be doing at "their age." They have lots of company to prove they are in the right groove.

Alternative to retirement: Your "bolt of life"

Okay, so retirement is not the way to go if you want to Put Old on Hold. What's the logical alternative?

Simple. *Plan to live seamlessly.* Think about the four words in that directive. "Plan" "to live" "seamlessly." Those are significant words that mean exactly what they say.

If you want to Put Old on Hold, it's not going to happen because you want it to or because you'd like to or because you think it would be a good idea. Putting Old on Hold is possible only if you have a plan *and* a commitment to make that plan a reality. It's not work; it's not difficult. It just requires your ongoing attention. And that "plan" must include preparation for you "to live"

> Putting Old on Hold is possible only if you have a plan *and* a commitment to make that plan a reality.

productively and "seamlessly" – meaning without self-inflicted traumatic breaks, such as retirement, that can mess up your mind, your health and your life.

Think of your life as a bolt of beautiful red satin cloth, unfolding seamlessly before you. (You don't like red? – whatever color you prefer is okay.) Satin allows you to shape it and drape it however you like – like life itself. Let's say there are approximately 100 yards on the bolt. You don't know for sure the actual number of yards because there isn't an accurate way to determine the length just by looking at it. In that respect, it's like life – you just don't know when or where the end will be reached. Let's unfurl the cloth 10 yards at a time and assign each 10 yards a decade of your life. This is about the way your life unfolds, in a general way:

From birth to age 20, you are getting set up for life. At age 20 you are in school preparing for a specific career or starting out in a job that will launch one of several careers.

At age 30, you are working on your career, married, buying a home and maybe starting a family.

At age 40, you are advancing in your career and raising kids. If you are smart, and you are, you will avoid having an unproductive "mid-life crisis" of any kind.

So far, you've unfurled 40 yards of material – that part of life you've lived so far. It's gone; you can't get it back and probably wouldn't want to. I hope you've grown in wisdom and maturity because you are going to need those virtues later on.

At 50, things begin to change dramatically. Change can be scary for wimps, but you are not a wimp. You are tough and will face the future with joy and

> You are tough and will face the future with joy and anticipation of the best yet to come.

anticipation of the best yet to come. You will ignore the marketers just waiting for you to turn 50 because they've got a lot to sell you in preparation for your "final years."

Here are five things sure to occur when you reach 50, all suggesting "the end is near":

1. You receive an invitation to join AARP. When that happens, you will return it unopened, marked "return to sender." Nothing wrong with AARP – maybe you'll consider it later on. You might, however, take a look at their new magazine just for 50-60 year-olds.

2. Real estate agents will come calling, wanting to sell you a retirement villa in Heavenly Hills – the land of the living dead. After all, it's a given you will retire and, surely, you will want to retire with your peers.

3. Insurance agents will try to sell you a policy to provide for your "final expenses." You certainly don't want your loved ones left financially holding the bag, or coffin, as the case may be.

4. Financial planners call during your dinner hour, wanting to sell you a great annuity so you'll have a cushy retirement. See, I told you retirement is big business!

5. But you know it's all over when the twinkie who takes your order for coffee and a greasy burger at the fast food emporium scrutinizes your wrinkles and asks, "Will that be senior coffee, ma'am?"

Pay no attention to those who imply your life will soon be over just because you've hit 50. It's not over – far from it.

Instead of listening to death and decrepitude mongers, immediately get your defiant attitude in gear and begin taking these steps:

> Pay no attention to those who imply your life will soon be over just because you've hit 50.

1. If you haven't done so already, stop fooling around and start taking responsibility for optimizing your health. You are only 50 or thereabouts, and even if you are older, much older, remember how incredibly forgiving your body can be once you decide to start treating it right.

2. Decide to live your life abundantly – all of it. That is truly a monumental decision, and it's not for everybody because everybody doesn't have what it takes. But you do!

3. Develop a plan to stay productive for the rest of your life. That may mean saving like crazy to start your own business so that when your current employer shows you the door at 65, you can smile in anticipation of the beginning of your Second Life. Yes, financial planning is crucial for future success – but instead of calling it retirement planning, call it future planning, or Second Life planning. If you persist in calling it retirement

planning, you may end up not saving as much as you might because of the negative connotation of the word "retirement." Yes, calling it "retirement planning" may indeed put a damper on your financial accumulation.

Or your plan may mean saving to enable you to go back to school full-time for an advanced degree or training for the career of your dreams. Ridiculous? Only if you've been listening to nay sayers who tell you it can't be done or is a waste of time. Remember, chronological age doesn't matter. Look at it this way. If at age 65 you go back to school, spend five years in preparation and stay in excellent health to 95 or 100 or more – will it have been wasted time? Of course not. You will have 25 or more years to improve the quality of your life and, probably, the lives of countless others.

If you think such a suggestion is pie-in-the-sky stuff or if you are not convinced of the soundness of such an idea, think about this: The California Policy Research Center report (mentioned earlier) dealing with the anticipated huge increase in Californians over 65 recommends providing college scholarships to help older Californians prepare for new careers. With this exciting information, I rest my case. It's selfish to hide your ageless talents under a bushel. Get them out there. Let them light up and improve the world.

Believe it! Fifty is not a harbinger of death. It's an opportunity to look forward to the best years of your life – an unprecedented Second Life.

Back to the bolt of red satin: You've lived another 10 years so let's

> Fifty is not a harbinger of death. It's an opportunity to look forward to the best years of your life – an unprecedented Second Life.

unwind another 10 yards. Here you are at age 60, getting ready to rock and roll because, for the past 10 years, you have been preparing eagerly and joyfully for your new life – your Second Life.

You will thumb your nose at tradition that says it's time to retire. You will not cave in to custom and cut the cloth and say: "This is all the life I want to live productively." You don't know how many yards of cloth remain on the bolt and you really don't care. You are ready to go on, seamlessly, without trauma, building, growing and living fully, unconcerned about the number of years you may have left. You have drafted your will and made other appropriate legal preparations. You are going to get on with living as if you will live forever. You will ignore the numbers. You will LIVE your life. ALL OF IT!

Bottom line about retirement

The bottom line about retirement is this: If you still think retirement may be the right thing for you, but you'd like a second opinion, please read *Retirement is Over-Rated* by Donald R. Germann, M.D. (Check the Resources section.) He's a radiologist, 70-something, who decided retirement was not for him (several times) and went back to work. He'll not only motivate and inspire you; he'll answer a lot of "insider" questions you've always wanted to ask about health care costs and Social Security but didn't know to ask. He is candid and down-to-earth; he writes in an engaging, easy-to-read style.

Remember: The human psyche maintains integrity and health when it is engaged in challenging, valuable activity and extremely goal-directed behavior. That's when you stay accountable to someone or something outside yourself, regardless of age.

> Remember: The human psyche maintains integrity and health when it is engaged in challenging, valuable activity and extremely goal-directed behavior.

Therefore . . .

- Above all, get, guard and maintain optimum health.
- Right now, plan to live ALL of your life – seamlessly.
- Establish long-range goals. Goals promote healthy longevity.
- Create a plan to stay productive and implement it.
- Do not invite emotional turmoil that comes with unnecessary traumatic change.

Attitudes, Tools and Advice

Overview

What contributes to getting old? Two things that are interconnected: 1. Attitude and 2. Giving up – letting youth go without a fight, not staying aware, not paying attention to how you are changing.

About attitude: You've heard it so often, you don't pay attention when you hear it: *Attitude is everything.* Repeat it over and over until it becomes a part of your daily approach to living. During the day when you *know* you are cranky or impatient, pull

> Attitude is everything. Repeat it over and over until it becomes a part of your daily approach to living.

yourself back to reality by reminding yourself *your* behavior is *your* choice. You can choose how to respond to the irritating person or situation. Anyone who works with the public becomes very proficient at this, and you can do it too, as you cope with your personal problems *and* the "problem of aging." Sorry, aging is not a problem unless you allow it to be. Choose to make it an opportunity to defy the odds and achieve your goal to Put Old on Hold. Attitude is everything.

About letting youth go without a fight: Treating youth like money – not keeping track of how it's spent – results in a loss of youthful characteristics. When you are young, youth is taken for granted. You do not appreciate this priceless treasure. You waste it, squander it, ignore it and abuse it. The trick is to be aware of the treasure early on and take steps to protect and maintain it.

I'd like you to think of youth as a beautiful silver vase. It's a gift you've been given. Your parents loved you enough to let you keep it when they discovered you were on the way. When it's new, youth is shiny and gleaming without too many imperfections. You assume it's going to stay that way forever, but if you don't take care of it, as the years go by, the tarnish builds up imperceptibly when you aren't looking. Of course the shine can be restored, but it takes some effort. At that point, something more important usually takes precedence.

It's the same with your body. One day, you look in the mirror and see a reflection you've never seen before. It can't be the same body you've been living in all these years, or is it? Yes, it is, and it's tarnished, big time! You move closer to the reflection to be certain you are seeing what you think you see. Up close, it's even worse. You hold your head in your hands and exclaim, "Oh my goodness, I look terrible. How did this happen!" It happened because you let go – you didn't pay attention to how you were changing. Yes, you are wearing dresses or pants a couple of sizes larger, but you didn't realize it had gotten out of hand so badly. So you resolve to take a stab at restoration. You sign up at the fitness center, but after three months of grunting, groaning, sweating and living on a crash diet, you realize how much work it is and say, "Oh well, it's too far gone. And besides, I don't have time to deal with it. I'll just accept me the way I am." And you do. And the downward spiral into decline continues. The tarnish gets darker and darker and eventually old age gets the upper hand. Youth is defiant and arrogant. Your job is to harness it, tame it and control how it evolves into maturity.

Don't allow tarnish to gain a foothold. Take stock of the youthful characteristics you have right now, at whatever age you are right now. Restore what you can and maintain it constantly. Do not put off maintenance.

It can be done, and it's well worth the effort. Remember, old age is not a TV mini-series that's over in five nights. It can go on for a very long time – you're living longer, you know – and it won't be "prime time" unless you are in your prime. *You can do it!*

What contributes to getting old?
Lack of vision and expectation

Not too long ago, age 65 was about as long as people lived. That anyone could live to 85 was amazing. It is astounding how the average American lifespan is increasing. There are now more centenarians than ever, and their numbers continue to increase unabated. Isn't that exciting?

Will 100 be the maximum number of years you can expect to live? I don't think so. If 65 was the norm just a few short decades ago, why should anyone think 100 or more can't become the norm in the near future? Consider this: In California alone, it is expected the number of those aged 85 and older will increase 200 percent in the next 40 years. Very likely, you too, wherever you

> In California alone, it is expected the number of those aged 85 and older will increase 200 percent in the next 40 years.

live, will experience the benefits of this exciting longevity phenomenon.

Even if 100 becomes the norm, I believe accepting ANY number as the maximum number of years you can expect to live places limitations on planning, achievement and quality of life.

"Limitation thinking"

Unfortunately, most older people won't begin new projects because they think, "I'll never see the fruit of my labors – I just can't justify the expense of getting started on something I'll never finish." So instead of embarking on an exciting, challenging, longevity-enhancing project, they sit in their rocking chairs, mentally sucking their thumbs, feeling sorry for themselves and lamenting how little they've gotten out of life. They just wait for the Grim Reaper to come calling. You, of course, are not going to do that.

To help bolster your resolve to stay in the game and to play until you win it, consider the following inspirational items:

James Russell Wiggins, at 95, is editor of the *Ellsworth American*, a weekly newspaper in Ellsworth, Maine. What a guy. He thinks retirement is a ridiculous waste of labor and talent. To him, it's alarming to see people in their 60s, in full possession of their faculties, lolling around retirement communities, giving in to lassitude. "How can society support such idleness?" he laments. (*Los Angeles Times*, May 5, 1999)

Sadie Lynette, 91, owns Lynette Antiques, a 1400-square-foot shop she runs by herself in Long Beach, California. She works four to five days a week, seven hours a day and does all her own bookkeeping. The shop has been in operation for 26 years and she takes pride in doing business the old-fashioned way – which she considers a secret of her success. If a customer isn't satisfied with a purchase, she offers a refund or exchange.

She says working keeps her healthy and chides "old ladies" who sit home and watch TV all day long, wasting time. She takes a lot of vitamins "even though doctors don't agree with them" and is convinced supplements are responsible for her good health and longevity. She does her own cooking, shopping and house-keeping. She has given up driving and relies on a loving grandson to take her to work and bring her home every day. He also takes her shopping. Her children are of retirement age but remain active – "chips off the old block." I spoke with Sadie and I can tell you she is an absolute inspiration. If I didn't know her age, I'd never guess her age. Her voice is strong, youthful and clear; her thoughts and words come without hesitation. There is nothing "old" about her. Her mental and speech acuity are consistent hallmarks of much older people who stay challenged and productive.

At 82, radio legend Paul Harvey signed a 10-year, $100 million contract with ABC. Why would ABC make such a "foolish" gamble? Harvey claims he lied about his age. "I told them I was 55." His doctor confirmed his excellent health and authorized him to become an astronaut. Why would Harvey want to commit himself to another 10 years of what he has done for the past 50 years? "I'd hate to get up every morning to play golf, the way I play golf." As for retirement, it's out of the question. (*Fortune*, December 18, 2000) Work is keeping Harvey young – to look at him you'd never guess his age.

Pauline Trigere, 92, fashion designer to celebrities and dignitaries including the Duchess of Windsor, has teamed with Gold Violin, a mail order catalog company that sells mid-to-high-end products exclusively for older adults. Trigere's collection includes everything from walking sticks to a hearing-aid case.

In Carlsbad, California, 78-year old Wally Taibleson is working toward a bachelor's degree in history from California State University. Why does he do it? Because he can and he wants to. Or, according to his son, "We have a running joke that in order to be employable, he really needs that degree." Mr. Taibleson expects to complete his degree in the spring of 2002, then possibly go on to a Ph.D. (*San Diego Union Tribune*, December 14, 2000)

In an average month, 3.7 percent of people aged 90 or above – at least 50,000 people – are in the U.S. workforce. (*Los Angeles Times*, May 5, 1999) Think about that – it's awesome. Not too many years ago, that was unheard of. People just didn't live that long and, if they did, they weren't working. They were curiosities in nursing homes or confined to wheelchairs, frail and barely hanging on to life.

The American Medical Association has identified at least 1,200 physicians aged 90 and above who still see patients. And why shouldn't they if they can still provide high quality care? Their mental, physical and professional proficiency does not hinge on a chronological number. If they can keep up their skills by engaging in mandatory continuing education then stay current with new developments, that's what counts.

Some time ago, I interviewed Cliff Holliday, a gentlemen who, at 100, went to work every day solving problems for seniors at the California Congress of Seniors in Los Angeles. I never met him, but speaking with him on the phone, I'd never guess he was 100. His voice was strong and vibrant. He spoke clearly and quickly, and attributed his youthfulness to getting up and going to work every day. It was common for him to work until midnight, then get up early and take the bus to work. What an inspiring role model. It made me feel so good to talk to him. He gave me hope for MY ability to persist and stay productive at an advanced age.

A personal friend of ours is 80, but you'd never believe it to look at or speak with him. He's been creating miniature model trains that are different and superior to what's available. While he's working on perfecting his project, he's looking for financing to start a new company to market his product. Remember, he's 80 and with significant health problems. But that's not keeping him from planning and looking to the future. He is Putting Old on Hold in a big way. What an inspiration.

Whatever you do, please do not engage in "limitation thinking." To do so is to play God and that's a waste of time. Regardless of your chronological age, fulfill your dreams to the best of your ability. You may surprise yourself and achieve far more than anything you could imagine.

> Regardless of your chronological age, fulfill your dreams to the best of your ability. You may surprise yourself and achieve far more than anything you could imagine.

The Deadly Sins of Negative Self Talk

Negative self-talk bothers me a lot because it is so destructive. If you realized how it hastens decline, you wouldn't indulge in it. When I hear it, it gets my back up so badly I automatically assume the persona of Judge Judy at her meanest. I become preachy and extremely pious. At that point, I am not above chastising a perfect stranger (with a smile, of course) for assaulting my ears with the utterance of one of "The Deadly Sins of Negative Self Talk."

Brothers and sisters, we are gathered here together to learn how to Put Old on Hold. If you want salvation from debilitating old age, you will avoid committing The Deadly Sins of

Negative Self Talk. Own up to those you admit to, do the penance prescribed and move on to enjoy the blessings of a long productive life.

A few of "The Deadly Sins of Negative Self Talk" are:

- ☒ I must be getting old

- ☒ I'm too old to be doing that

- ☒ I'm too old to learn that

- ☒ I'm just an "old broad"

- ☒ I'm having a "senior moment"

- ☒ I'm a senior and deserve special perks

I must be getting old

How often have you said, "I must be getting old" when you drop something or do something klutzy? It's devastating – not that you dropped something but that you chastise yourself for doing what everybody does, regardless of age. Negative self talk will get you into decline, deterioration and decrepitude faster than you can imagine. If you want to Put Old on Hold, please don't beat up on yourself for exhibiting human frailty.

> If you want to Put Old on Hold, please don't beat up on yourself for exhibiting human frailty.

The subconscious is so powerful and obedient. It will believe anything you tell it, and it can't differentiate between fact and fiction. It listens and acts upon exactly what you think and tell yourself.

For your penance:

Next time you drop something, don't tell yourself you are "getting old." Get a new attitude! Bend over, pick it up and exclaim how good it feels to be able to bend and stretch. If it feels especially good, drop it again and pick it up with the other hand so you get a workout. Misplace something? Be patient with yourself instead of immediately and relentlessly chastising yourself about "getting old." Don't assume you have Alzheimer's or that you are "losing it" until and unless it's medically diagnosed by an expert. Don't "force" yourself to remember – relax – it will come to you sooner or later. If something has eluded you all day, right before you go to bed, think about it, even write it down and ask your subconscious to help you remember. The answer may come to you in the middle of the night when you get up to go to the bathroom. Your mind will be relaxed, allowing the "answer" to pop into your head. It's not magic or anything esoteric. Your mind and body will do what you want it to do if you give it a chance.

In between klutzy occurrences, tell yourself you are not getting old, you're getting better. You'll have fewer mishaps and enhance your ability to Put Old on Hold at the same time.

I'm too old to be doing that

Committing this sin is a major offense against yourself. I'll bet you do it not because you really believe you are too old, but because you think that's what you are supposed to say because you are at "that age." You know within yourself what you are capable of doing – chronological age be damned.

> You know within yourself what you are capable of doing – chronological age be damned.

The wife of a friend I used to work with died suddenly. While working with him, he used to talk about all the "Walter Mitty" kinds of things he wanted to do, such as sailing, hang gliding and other "daring" activities. He never did those things because his wife discouraged him – which was understandable because she was concerned for his safety. Sometime after her death, I received a note from him telling me what he had been doing. It included more than a few of the forbidden things he had always wanted to do. Then, in parentheses, he added, "I guess I should be acting my age." At 52? I don't think so! I verbally smacked him on the side of the head a couple of times, and I suspect he will never again think he is too old to do whatever he wants to do and knows he can do.

For your penance:

Get a notebook and write down 25 positive affirmations for every negative "I can't or shouldn't do that" that comes into your head. Whatever traditions, customs or well-meaning friends say you shouldn't do "at your age," think of why you should do it and write that statement down 25 times. Or write it as many times as it takes to find the courage to do what YOU want to do and know you are capable of doing.

I'm too old to learn that

I often hear an older person say this when faced with a new challenge. When a new computer program was installed at work, an older (but

> Age has nothing to do with ability to learn.

younger than I) pharmacist complained, "I'm too old to be learning this." No, he's not too old. Lazy, perhaps, but not too old. Age has nothing to do with ability to learn. Actually, he's just biding his time until – you guessed it – retirement. Putting Old on Hold is not on his agenda. I guess that's okay – for him.

For your penance:

Sign up for a class to learn something you imagine you are "too old" to learn. Your success will make you feel younger, bolster your self-esteem and increase your faith in your ability to tackle anything you put your mind to, regardless of your age.

I'm just an "old broad"

Please, don't ever refer to yourself as an "old broad." If you do, I'll hunt you down, call Judge Judy and have you committed to a retirement community where you can happily commiserate with real old broads, and you won't be happy. "Old broad" is a dreadfully demeaning term. An article in the *San Diego Union Tribune* (October 24, 2000) reported about a two-hour TV film in the works, titled "These Old Broads"[1] in which Elizabeth Taylor, 68, Shirley MacLaine, 66, and Debbie Reynolds, 68, mock themselves and their public image. It's too bad these ladies hold themselves and their place in life in such low esteem. These women are not "old broads" – they are women of tremendous value; they are role models and survivors in the best sense of the word.

The article negatively portrayed Debbie Reynolds as the owner of a "pathetic hotel, where she displays her old costumes and sings in the casino." I've been in Debbie Reynolds' "pathetic hotel" and I can tell you what she has done with it is awesome. Ruined financially by several husbands, she's bounced back to make a life for herself and is an inspiration for all women regardless of age. She has learned to Put Old on Hold big time. "Old Broad" indeed!

For your penance:

Don't wait for the next time the conditioned reflex to call yourself an "old broad" kicks in. Every morning, put your best face on, then get dressed and ready to astound the world with your ageless uniqueness. Pretend movie star Fernando Lamas, the legendary charming rascal, is next to you, cooing into your ear the outrageous line he handed every woman he met,

---

1 Aired February, 2001

"Dahling, you look mah-vel-ous." If you have never heard of Fernando Lamas, it doesn't matter. His appreciation of feminine pulchritude made women feel special and that is what counts. Don't ever leave the house without telling yourself how "mah-vel-ous" you are.

> Don't ever leave the house without telling yourself how "mah-vel-ous" you are.

I'm having a "senior moment"

I hear this frequently and consider it extremely destructive. A fiftyish customer came in to ask for a prescription refill but couldn't remember the name of her medication. She laughed and held her head while wailing, "Excuse me, I'm having a senior moment!" Because I know her rather well, I scolded her for berating her ability to remember and pointed out that bright young people sometimes forget things too, but I've never heard one of them excuse a memory lapse with "I'm having a junior moment." And that's as it should be. Instead of laying claim to a "senior moment," just pause for a second, wait for the stress and fear of losing your memory to abate, then allow yourself to remember.

For your penance:

You have a lot on your mind, so get organized and write down what you want to remember. Carry a notebook and pen with you and use them. There is no shame in making lists and notes. The most successful and productive people, regardless of

> Get organized and write down what you want to remember. Carry a notebook and pen with you and use them.

age, do it all the time. The next time you have a momentary memory lapse, recognize it as a manifestation of stress. In no case are you to accuse yourself of having a "senior moment."

Everyone forgets. Don't hasten decline by telling yourself you are "losing it." Remember, the subconscious obediently acts on whatever you tell it and will help make it reality. Instead, focus on Putting Old on Hold.

I'm a senior and I deserve special perks.

The age at which one becomes a "senior" is dropping to 55, and even younger, so it's not uncommon for Boomers to fall into this sin early in the aging process, particularly since it is now accepted that "with age comes privilege." Regardless of accepted norms, once you see yourself as deserving of special consideration because of your age (and for no other good reason), you are an aging sinner, big time! Listen up: It's only by the grace of God you are living so long. Why expect a reward for reaching 60, 70 or beyond? Even if you've taken stellar care of your health, you still can't take full credit for your longevity. Life can and does end in an instant regardless of how you have lived. The other thing is this: Asking for or expecting special treatment invites pity and, as you age, that's the last thing you need or want. It leads to development of a pauper mentality. You start to imagine your age entitles you to any and everything, and you begin to act accordingly. Hard-up behavior ultimately affects how others regard and treat you. Once you start asking for anything you don't really need or deserve, it damages your self-respect and hastens the decline and loss of personal power. If you are already "doing it" – stop it before it becomes deeply ingrained. Don't begin to see age-related perks as a right or entitlement. Self-respect is more important than asking for or taking what you don't really need.

> Don't begin to see age-related perks as a right or entitlement. Self-respect is more important than asking for or taking what you don't really need.

For your penance:

Be grateful for the gift of longevity and use it to help others less fortunate than you. Stifle a spirit of entitlement by going out of your way to help truly needy individuals get the assistance they need. By example, encourage others to have an independent "can do" attitude.

Avoiding The Deadly Sins of Negative Self Talk will help make your road to agelessness as smooth as silk. The sins mentioned aren't the only stumbling blocks – obviously, there are others. Be aware of them, rebuke them and avoid them as you would the plague. Lovingly chastise others who are guilty of indulging in them. Remind them and yourself that, to Put Old on Hold, saying negative things about yourself or your ability is not acceptable.

> Limiting social contact to those of your own age hastens decline.

Limiting contacts to peers

Limiting social contact to those of your own age hastens decline. Becoming isolated and insulated in a "seniors only" enclave or otherwise avoiding interaction with younger people is a sure-fire way to slide into old age. I know how popular these communities are and a lot of people are happy living in them, but I don't think it's the healthiest way to live. You tend to emulate the thinking and behavior of those with whom you associate most often. If you regularly socialize exclusively with people who look, think and act old, you will "catch" the "old" virus that emanates from them.

> Everyone benefits from the energy, excitement, vision and, yes, the immaturity of youth.

Everyone benefits from the energy, excitement, vision and, yes, the immaturity of youth. Sure, young people are obnoxious at times, maybe even a lot of the time, but so are old people. You'd understand this better if you dealt with old people who deliberately yank you around and, when they see they've made you irritated, will coyly snicker, "Aren't us old people a pain in the neck?"

Case in point: A customer who could charitably be called a shrewd old codger was trying to get his prescription filled using an expired insurance card. He knew it was inactive but held back new insurance information because he thought his new co-pay was higher. Finally agreeing his old insurance had been terminated, he reluctantly pulled out his new insurance card. To his delight and surprise, his new insurance didn't have a co-pay at all. That's when he made the remark, "Aren't we old people a pain in the neck?" It happens often. Sure, young people can be just as wily, but at least they don't blame it on their youth. Frankly, I'd rather be around young people who have a fresh, outrageous outlook on life than around old people wrapped up in their often unrealistic concerns. Young people give inspiretion and hope for the future. And they need us as mentors. Their floundering and immaturity beg for mature adults to guide them with wisdom, experience and love. We can provide this guidance and we'll all be better for it.

Not trusting your own ability

It's common for some older people to lose the courage to stand on their own two feet. Instead, they ask or expect others to do for them what they could do for themselves. I have a customer, a little old lady (yes, she describes herself as a little old lady) who is just as sharp as a tack, but never shops without "her girl" (who is almost as old as she is) to help her write checks. She complains she gets nervous and her hand wobbles. There is nothing wrong with her writing, but she depends on "her girl" to help her. She takes pride in having someone do things for her. Suggestion: Put Old on Hold and be your own "girl" or "boy" as long as you can.

Ever hear of child-proof caps? Unless a customer wants an ordinary "easy-off" cap and signs a form absolving the pharmacy of liability if it gets in the hands of a child and results in a problem, all dispensed prescriptions must have a child-proof cap. They may be difficult to get off unless you know how. Like most other things, it's easy when you know what to do. "I don't have the strength," is a common complaint. "I have to ask my grandchildren to help me."

If you can lift a fork, you can manage a child-proof cap. I will make an allowance for really weak, frail individuals – but you are neither weak nor frail so decide right now that child-proof caps will not bamboozle you today or in the future. Just hold the bottle in one hand and, with the other hand, simultaneously press down on the cap and turn it counter clockwise. Voila, it's off. Practice makes perfect. Even though I demonstrate how easy it is, many people, including big strong men, resist being self-sufficient. "Don't bother to show me how to do it – just give me an easy-off cap."

> Take pride in accepting responsibility for yourself and trusting your ability to learn. Staying mentally strong will enhance your ability to Put Old on Hold.

Knowledge is power and knowing how to do simple things may be a lifesaver. Take pride in accepting responsibility for yourself and trusting your ability to learn. Staying mentally strong will enhance your ability to Put Old on Hold.

Another thing: Please do not allow loving family and friends to suggest "you don't have to do that anymore; we'll do it for you." They mean well and it's tempting to let others do for you. But if you can do for yourself, thank them for their concern and, with all the kindness you can muster, let them know you are not senile and can still take care of yourself. Staying strong provides a benefit for them as well. You show that when they reach your age, they can and should be tough and independent, too. Killing loved ones with kindness often starts as early as age 50. It's not because they think of you as particularly needy; it's born of love and concern and a sense that "it's our turn to take care of you." It's a nice warm 'n fuzzy thing to want to do for relatives and friends, but will not help them Put Old on Hold.

How to counteract getting old

Exercise

Exercise is essential. Even though the importance of exercise is common knowledge, some women are afraid to work out. Dr. Sandra O'Brien Cousins, a professor of Physical Education and Recreation at the University of Alberta, surveyed more than 300 women over the age of 70 about the benefits and risks of fitness activities. Respondents recognized the benefits of exercise but had strong reservations. Comments included: "My heart would hemorrhage." "Muscle seizure." "I would be carried out on a stretcher." Some just flat out feared death as a risk of exercising.

Recently I met a stunning, slim woman in her late 50s. In our discussion about successful aging, she said although she exercised and was in excellent physical condition, she was careful not to do anything that might cause injury. For example, the last time she cleaned windows – they were the lift-out kind – they seemed terribly heavy and she decided then and there it would be the last time she would do that chore. Personally, I don't blame her for not wanting to clean windows ever again – why bother, it's a thankless job and they just get dirty again. Even as I understand her desire not to injure herself – it's certainly a legitimate concern – does she have the best attitude? She could have said instead, "I need to do more strength training. There is no reason why this job should be any more difficult than it used to be."

Putting Old on Hold is about choices. It's about meeting challenges head on and taking sensible risks. I can't judge whether she made the right decision to never clean windows again for fear of injury. I can only see the end result – she is letting go of a youthful characteristic without a fight and forfeiting maintenance of a certain level of physical strength without thinking of long-range consequences. She is giving up an opportunity to make a choice that will help maintain her strong mind and body, and enhance her ability to Put Old on Hold.

> Putting Old on Hold is about choices. It's about meeting challenges head on and taking sensible risks.

I've made a decision to stay strong in every way I possibly can. I lift weights and walk on a treadmill several times a week for 30 minutes at a high rate of speed. This enables me to move quickly and with assurance. Walking and weight training are two ways I avoid osteoporosis and maintain a high level of physical flexibility.

When I see people my age tottering unsurely and meandering along on a cane, I feel terribly sad. Being quick on your feet is a benefit at any age and it's especially important if you want to Put Old on Hold.

> Being quick on your feet is a benefit at any age and it's especially important if you want to Put Old on Hold.

A labored, uncertain step indicates decline and old age, a conclusion confirmed in a survey of 200 people whose ages ranged from 18 to 80 ("Putting Off Aging" by Betty Weir

Alderson in *Rx Remedy*, May/June 2000). Several teenagers found "attitude" and "behavior" the most significant markers of age. Only seven of the 200 considered hair color one of the things that makes them think someone is old. Wrinkles were checked only slightly more frequently. However, the way people move turned out to be significant. Almost every one considered becoming "inactive," "stooped," "unsteady," "having poor posture" and "walking slowly" some of the most common characteristics of "old." So you've been told. Youthful, erect, confident, sprightly movement is a hallmark of those who Put Old on Hold.

> Youthful, erect, confident, sprightly movement is a hallmark of those who Put Old on Hold!

Have you ever reclined on a slant board? If you haven't, you don't know what you are missing. You can make one inexpensively. Go to your lumberyard and ask them to cut a piece of ¾ inch plywood – long enough to lie on and wide enough for your body. Prop up one end about 12 inches from the floor. Put a mat or rug on it and stretch out on it for 30 minutes. The results are amazing. Everything goes back into place, including your facial muscles, and eventually you fall into a state of total relaxation. After you are calm and tranquil, do some exercises to help strengthen and flatten your abdominal muscles. A slant board is a dynamite Put Old on Hold "secret weapon." You get a lot of benefit for very little effort. Check with your doctor first if you think it may not be right for you.

Yoga: In my 30s, I started doing Yoga exercises with Richard Hittleman on TV. It's an interesting thing about Yoga – long after you stop doing the positions, the body remembers what it was taught so it's easy to restart or continue stretching routines learned years earlier. To this day the most comfortable way for me to sit is in the lotus position. Stretching should be a part of any exercise routine. (Check with your doctor before starting any exercise routine.)

Facial exercise: Exercising the muscles in your face is just as important as exercising the rest of your body. There are many facial exercise books and regimens available but the one I like is Carol Maggio's *Facercise* program. She has a video in which she goes through a series of exercises with you. (I've included information about her program in the Resources section.)

Exercise your mind: One of the best mind and brain builders is crossword puzzles. Do them at every opportunity. Do them while you are watching mindless, boring TV, waiting for an appointment or enjoying a few minutes of down time. If

> One of the best mind and brain builders is crossword puzzles.

you've never done one, don't start out with a difficult puzzle from the *New York Times*. Start with something easy and work your way up to advanced puzzles. Choose reading materials that make you think and challenge you to expand your world view. Your brain is not nearly as overloaded as you might imagine. There is a lot more room for you to grow into an even more interesting, knowledgeable, productive human being. A sharp, agile mind is a hallmark of one who has Put Old on Hold.

Be a people watcher

Observation is a powerful teacher. Watch what people do and say that you consider "aging," then consciously avoid those behaviors. Notice how people at different stages and ages dress and take care of personal grooming. Listen to how they speak and what they talk about. Watch how they move. Just observing others will motivate you to examine and monitor your own thinking, attitudes and behaviors, and help you do what's necessary to Put Old on Hold.

Constantly look for inspiring role models

Your thinking and behavior develop in direct proportion to the number of stimulating images you see, so actively look for them. Constantly feeding your brain and subconscious with inspiring thoughts and pictures will positively influence your attitudes and behaviors and help you Put Old on Hold. You can find wonderful role models in your own life and there are many veteran icons in the media to emulate.

Ageless Barbara Walters and indefatigable Elizabeth Dole are certainly inspiring. While campaigning on behalf of her husband's bid for the presidency, I recall Mrs. Dole's charismatic public speaking skills and the warmth and genuineness she projected. She's a favorite role model.

I am especially in awe of 83-year old Mike Wallace. I recently watched Mike being interviewed by Tim Russert and could not keep my eyes off the TV screen as I tried to figure out what it was about this man that makes him appear twenty years younger. Physically and mentally he is unlike any other 83-year old I have ever seen. His youthful vivacity, animation and energy are seldom found in someone his age. Why the disparity between his chronological age and his young-looking physical appearance and outstanding mental agility? One reason may be that he is living "seamlessly" To my knowledge he has never retired, even temporarily. Had he done so during that period, I think he would have lost a lot of youthful characteristics.

Another explanation for his staying power may be his ability to look at events through "fresh eyes." On a couple of occasions, I have heard him mention how much he values the perspective found in the "fresh eyes" of young people. This confirms my belief, stated elsewhere in this book, that to remain ageless it's important to maintain contact with younger people and appreciate what they have to offer. The value of the point of view found in their "fresh eyes" could give balance and a new outlook to unintended inflexible thinking. It's not necessary to accept what those "fresh eyes" see or advocate, what's important is to be willing to at least try to understand *"how, what and why"* those "fresh eyes" see as they do. It will help anyone stay as young as Mike Wallace.

In my 30s, thanks to Jack LaLanne's exercise program on TV, I started working out. Accompanied by his beautiful white dog Happy, I can still see Jack clearly, a mass of rippling muscles, oozing testosterone, bending and stretching, energetically jumping up and down, whistling and having a great time. I'll never forget what he wore – what appeared to be ballet slippers and a body-hugging jumpsuit that showed off his exquisitely chiseled physique and, above all, pencil-slim hips. Oh, how I envied those hips! I still do many of the exercises he did on his TV program, trying to whittle down my hips. Have I succeeded? If you ask my devoted husband, he will tell you I have the body of a goddess, but then, he's into science fiction. If you ask my friend Peggy, she will tell you my hips are to die for but, given the circumference of her hips, she's ready to die for any hips that are even a tad tighter than hers. The truth is, I do not have Jack's pencil-slim hips, but that's okay because I'm a work in progress. I will never stop trying, thanks to the enduring inspiration of a truly effective role model.

Jack achieved his good health and physical condition through hard work and determination. I doubt he relied on the kind of gimmicky paraphernalia sold by exercise gurus today. On his program, Jack used a chair to help perform exercises. He didn't sell pricey exercise gadgets that quickly wind up in a garage sale. To help with stretching, he did sell a rubber cord that looked like a jump rope, which I bought, still have, and is as good as new (like Jack himself). If you've seen him on TV recently, you know what a phenomenon he is. In his 80s, he's just as tight and trim as ever and, yes, he still has those pencil-slim hips and still oozes testosterone. He's a powerful inspiretion. When I see him I think, "When I get to his age, I can look and feel just as good as he does." You have no idea how great it feels at age 70-plus to be able to say, "When I get to his age . . . " To have something to look forward to achieving that you know is possible can be a great motivator. Jack proves a Second Life exists for those who want it and are willing to do what it takes to get it and hold on to it. I hope he lives forever!

Start keeping a journal and/or scrapbook of people who inspire you, documenting what it is about them that motivates you to reach your goals. Read your list frequently and continue to add more ageless heroes to it. The more role models you have, the better. Staying aware of the success of others will help you achieve your goals. If they can do it, you can too.

Mentor generously and be a positive role model

Help others grow to be ageless. Discover the "youthifying" power in the feedback you receive when you make a difference in the life of someone else. Giving of yourself is the ultimate selfishness because you, the giver, always receive more than the recipient.

I recently had a super youthifying experience. I was profiled in the September 2000 issue of *Life Extension* magazine. In a letter to the editor the following month, a woman wrote to say how much she appreciated learning about me and how much it helped her. When I first read that magical letter, my endorphins kicked into high gear because I realized how positively I had touched the life of another. I felt fantastic. I am convinced

> Giving of yourself is the ultimate selfishness because you, the giver, always receive more than the recipient.

that, for a brief period of time after I read her letter, my aging process had stopped and regeneration had taken place.

So I encourage you to have as many positive, giving, youthifying experiences as possible. It's the closest thing to real magic you will ever know.

Maintain an inventory of your skills

Constantly evaluate your mental and physical abilities. Keep a running inventory of skills you consider important for staying young. Take necessary steps to maintain and improve them. For example, can you still:

- Breathlessly climb a flight of stairs?
- Walk as quickly as you did a year ago?
- Bend and touch your toes?

Was there anything you could do even six months ago you can no longer do? If so, can you regain that ability with some effort?

If a skill or ability has become inactive, please don't take for granted it's gone forever. Assuming you lost a particular youthful characteristic by default (meaning through laziness or inattention), start working slowly to get it back. Be defiant about it. Don't tell yourself "it's too late" or "I'm too far gone." Just do it! I cannot begin to tell you how much little victories will do for your self-esteem. They add up, and you will come to a place in your life and in your mind where you will see yourself in an entirely different light. So will others. People will comment on the "evolving you." I challenge you to take a step-by-step approach to get to where you want to be. It works, and each step of improvement – given positive reinforcement by others as your progress becomes visible – is powerfully motivating. It propels you toward your goal.

Defy convention

Make a list of age-related taboos – activities, ideas or behaviors others might disparage. For example, would you like to take acting or voice lessons because, even at your "advanced" age, you still yearn to be a professional entertainer? You think that's not such a risky thing to do? In some families and communities, an older, seemingly "settled" person might be considered on the brink of senility for even entertaining such a dream, let alone trying to make it a reality. In my own family, I can recall when my oldest sister, in her 30s, told my mother she wanted to learn to tap dance. Mom's negative response devastated my sister. The subject never came up again and, of course, my sister never learned to tap dance for fear of incurring mom's displeasure. Mom should see me ice skating now!

Would you like to run for public office but fear public opinion might shoot you down because of your age? Ronald Reagan and Robert Dole were among the first to suffer the arrows of ageism, but they persisted. You can, too. Would you like to be a flight attendant – a job traditionally held by younger people? You could definitely go for this one – it's no longer necessary to be a cute blonde female under 25. Your friends and family may think you are crazy, but so what?

Would you like to have a relationship with an older/ younger person or with someone from another race or culture, but put it out of your mind because "how it would look" at your age? Ask yourself – are the "taboo" behaviors, ideas or activities you are considering actually illegal, immoral or unethical? Would they harm others or burden your conscience if you did them? If not, then get rid of the fear. Step up to the plate and take a swing at cultural or social no-nos. If booed by onlookers

> Defying convention when it doesn't make sense is effective ammunition in your arsenal of weapons to Put Old on Hold.

(who may secretly admire your daring), so what? It is both exhilarating and liberating to overcome obstacles. Defying convention when it doesn't make sense is effective ammunition in your arsenal of weapons to Put Old on Hold.

Believe this: You are not too old to do what you want to do and know you can do. Within reason, what your mind can conceive, you can achieve. The truth in that adage, heard so often, may have lost its originality, but I want you to adopt it as a "mantra." Silently repeat that mantra any time you are afraid to try something new because of "your age." You know within you what you are capable of doing. "I'm too old to do that" should never cross your mind, let alone your lips.

> Remember, "growing old" is a choice. The alternative choice is "staying young."

Remember, "growing old" is a choice. The alternative choice is "staying young." You can do it if you have a plan and stay in control of your health, thoughts, behavior and speech. As early in life as possible, consciously *choose* to do and think what will enhance your ageless, healthy longevity. Use this book as a guide and you'll make it.

Cultivate a sense of humor and a realistic perspective

The stuff you fret and fume about today won't even be a blur in your mind next week, so don't sweat it. So what if the dry cleaner loses your favorite shirt. It happened to me, and I was really angry about it for a whole week (what a waste of time and energy). But you know what? Now I don't even remember what the shirt looked like. What is the big deal about a "favorite" shirt or anything easily replaceable, anyway? The world is full of fantastic shirts, so I bought a new one. Was the lost shirt worth fuming and fussing over? No, because there was nothing I could do to get it back. Sue the dry cleaner? You are kidding, of course. At a time like this, a sense of humor and a reality check come in handy.

Get your head into gear about the realities of life. Unfortunate things do indeed happen to nice people and that's the way life is. The shirt I fumed over was small stuff. The lesson I learned and want to share with you is this: Looking at life in retrospect and realizing how silly you behave in a given situation should, ideally, happen only once in a blue moon. Learn to spot "small stuff situations" when they happen, deal with them immediately in a calm and rational manner, then get on with more positive things in your life. When a "small stuff situation" happens (assume it's all small stuff), question if it will likely be a major issue next week. Be brutally honest and ask yourself if you'll even remember it happened. People who want to Put Old on Hold keep that in mind and diligently live by it. It defuses a lot of stress and avoids unnecessary grief. And you'll have fewer "worry" lines engraved on your face.

Be kind and patient

Be kind and tolerant, particularly with those you love and especially toward those from whom you want service. Older people don't like to wait. They don't have a bus or plane to catch; they don't have to be some place at a specific time, but if made to wait, they can get very cranky. I haven't been able to figure out what makes old people behave so badly sometimes. For sure, when they don't feel well and things don't go their way,

> Be kind and tolerant, particularly with those you love and especially toward those from whom you want service.

it's easy to be nasty. I used to say it's because the portion of the brain that controls civilized behavior has turned to concrete, but obviously that's not what happens.

More likely it's the result of hardening of the arteries that impairs blood flow to the brain. It may just be a lifelong character defect that manifests more when you no longer care what people think about you. Or it may be bitterness and remorse over an unfulfilled life.

For men, I think negative personality changes are exacerbated by hormone decline, at least in part. Earlier I spoke about the importance of an annual comprehensive blood test called the CBC/Chemistry profile. This is not just for women – men need it, too. It can uncover potential problems, including hormonal, that may be easily corrected and result in a dramatic, positive personality change. But diminished testosterone doesn't affect all men equally. Some stay as sweet as pie, but others become totally nasty, belligerent monsters. Interesting, isn't it?

My way of dealing with difficult people is to get to know them on a first-name basis. Some of the nastiest people become pussycats when you establish a one-to-one relationship with them. It has proven to me it's not "old age" or hardened arteries or hormone loss that causes objectionable behavior – it's choice. People decide how they want to behave. It's as simple as that. Old people seem to make more negative behavior choices than younger people.

Resolve right now that you will always be a class act in the deportment department – it will go a long way toward helping you Put Old on Hold. Stay aware of how your behavior is changing and make a conscious effort to be rational at all times. If you have all your faculties intact, you can control your behavior. It will have a positive effect on the way others see and treat you.

> Stay aware of how your behavior is changing and make a conscious effort to be rational at all times.

Wear a pleasant expression

Discover the youthifying power that comes with a pleasant expression. It's not just the artistic quality of the Mona Lisa that captivates. It's the smile! Keeping the corners of your mouth upturned in a Mona Lisa smile will keep you looking young. When upturned, you are more attractive, there is a sparkle in your eyes and it's easier to think pleasant thoughts.

When out and about, try this experiment. As you pass people in the mall, make eye contact with your Mona Lisa smile in place and watch them smile back – sometimes with big toothy smiles. You'll make their day and their response will make yours. Try it with babies. In their innocence, they recognize the beauty in a friendly face and react accordingly. What is more wonderful than a baby who beams at you in response to your smiling visage? It's positive proof your Mona Lisa smile works wonders. It's non-threatening to look pleasant. It's a no-sweat way to help you and others Put Old on Hold. A possible bonus: You may even meet someone wonderful.

Don't play age games

If you think you look great for your age, please don't invite others to guess how old you are. It's a dead giveaway you're an old fogy. Nobody needs to know how old you are. You don't need to ask the question as a reality check to see how you are doing or how others perceive you. Just look around at younger people. By comparison, you can see for yourself how well you are doing. Remember, you shouldn't be dwelling on the numbers, anyway.

Alternatively, don't advertise your age. I had a customer who really looked good for his age, but he became a pain in the neck because every time he came in, he reminded everyone how old he was. He may have looked good, but his behavior gave away his age.

Always feel fantastic

If you have health problems, keep them between yourself and your doctor. Make an appointment and unload it all on him or her. Believe it or not, most people are not interested in the details of your angioplasty or how you nearly died in the operating room. They will listen politely and make all the appropriate "oh, how awful" sounds, but they would rather hear something else. Trust me on this!

When someone asks, "How are you?" please understand it's not an invitation to share your woes. Your stock answer should be "I'm fantastic." It will make the other person feel good and glad to see you. Believe it or not, you'll feel better too.

Keep your appearance contemporary

Always try to look *your* personal best. If "doing your own thing" relative to appearance really means wearing what everybody else is wearing, take a look at yourself in a mirror. Try to be objective. Is that outfit really right for you? I think almost everyone has that wee small voice within him or her that whispers, "That looks awful," or "You shouldn't be seen in public looking like that." If you hear that voice within, or if someone who loves you cares enough to tell you how you look, pay attention. Adapt, don't automatically adopt, what's current if it's not your style. Wear what's appropriate and pegs you as ageless. If you can pull that off, you'll be doing great!

Spare others the embarrassment of seeing your less-than-perfect bare body parts. One day I was amused and at the same time horrified to see an overweight Boomer, long salt-and-pepper hair (mostly yellowish white) in a teenage ponytail, wearing a revealing cut-off tank top. The rolls of fat hanging over her too-tight jeans were something to behold. She probably thought she looked hot or sexy or whatever – why else would she venture out of the house looking like that? The whole picture was a calling card that screamed, "I'm an aging Boomer in denial. Even if I look ridiculous, this is my way of staying young." Wear what you believe is right for you, but remember, the key is to shoot for agelessness.

> Adapt, don't automatically adopt, what's current if it's not your style. Wear what's appropriate and pegs you as ageless.

My thinking about public display of private body parts is this: Skinny teenagers may look "cute" with an exposed belly button, perhaps with a ring attached to it. (Ouch!) I don't look cute with my belly button hanging out and neither does any mature woman, even if she's in great shape. Flab-free teens may look cute in their short shorts. I don't, so I spare others the visual assault by covering up. Besides, I believe in Mystery. I would much rather have others wonder what it looks like "under there." (For the record, not cute – just phenomenal!)

Be a head turner in the best sense of the word. Reward others who are head turners. When you see someone who looks great, tell him or her. You'll be sure to make that person's day and yours as well.

> Be a head turner in the best sense of the word. Reward others who are head turners. When you see someone who looks great, tell him or her. You'll be sure to make that person's day and yours as well.

One day I was in line at a supermarket and a couple of lines away I noticed a woman who really looked nice – as if she had spent time thinking about her appearance. She wasn't overdone; she just looked put together. I asked the person in back of me to hold my place and I went over to her and said, "I just wanted to tell you that you look fantastic." She lit up like a thousand-watt light bulb and her husband, standing next to her, beaming with pride, nearly popped his shirt buttons. She thanked me profusely for making her day. Her reaction made mine as well. Sure, it's risky to walk up to people and comment on their appearance – they can always tell you to go away and mind your own business. But most people welcome kind comments from a stranger if they're really sincere and not intrusive.

Have a plan to constantly "upgrade" and improve your appearance. It's like owning a computer. All the bits and bytes work fine, but newer enhancements appear on the market like clockwork. Your computer may not need all the latest bells and whistles, but it's important to have some of them. It's the same with you. While you don't want to latch on to every fashion fad that comes along, use the best of what's new to reinvent yourself with a totally new look from time to time. I emphasize the importance of adapting rather than adopting. For example, if the latest thing in shoes makes your feet look deformed or gives the impression you are a bowlegged prehistoric cavewoman, search for the best among the worst of the "styles" or wait until designers start liking women again – and they will, sooner or later.

If you don't constantly upgrade and reinvent your appearance, you will forever look like you are stuck in the sixties, seventies or whatever. Don't wait for your kids or spouse to suggest you need a "makeover." Enhance and improve whenever something is available in the fashion world that will transform you into a "wow!" of a head turner. Remember, when you look appropriately contemporary, you look ageless – another great tool to help you Put Old on Hold. Will you be inviting envy? Maybe, but you'll be doing a good deed. You will be role modeling and inspiring your friends and peers to be their best. That's a real win-win situation!

Consider surgical enhancement – or don't!

Whether you choose to have cosmetic surgery of any kind depends on how satisfied you are with your appearance. It's an extremely personal decision. Not to mention costly. You should not allow anyone to talk you into or out of it. If you decide to do it, do so only after thorough research. To help you do it right, I recommend Susan Gail's book, *Cosmetic Surgery: Before, Between and After.* (It's listed in the Resources section.)

What you see in the mirror, how you perceive yourself, how you think you appear to the world affects your thinking and behavior. It will have a bearing on how well you ultimately Put Old on Hold.

Eventually you will do what you feel you need to do to enhance your appearance. I suggest you go about it in a thoughtful, organized way. When I was 69, I decided to get braces on my teeth. It was a fantastic experience. Let me explain how it came about.

I was born with "Cher" teeth – if you recall what hers looked like before she had them fixed. I grew up hating them, believing no one could possibly love me because they were so unattractive. (Obviously, my husband looked beyond the teeth when he decided to marry me.) When bonding became available, I was ecstatic – I could finally do "something" about those ugly teeth. Bonding helped a lot, but it wasn't the ultimate answer. After a time, the bonding wears off and you're right back where you started. The last dentist I consulted suggested braces as a first step to improvement. I thought he was crazy. After all, at 69? Was there another human being on earth who had teeth in braces at 69? Later on, I learned I was not a trend-setter. Others much older than I had braces on their teeth. I read about a woman, 90, in a nursing home who had her teeth straightened. A waste of time and money? Who cares? It's her life, they're her teeth and, frankly, I think it's great. Who knows how long she will live? Regardless, it will enhance her quality of life and make her more attractive. Many old people have terrible-looking teeth. You wouldn't want them to kiss you.

Long story short, I opted for getting the braces and, without question, it was the absolute best thing I've done so far to improve my appearance. It took just 18 months of some discomfort a lot of the time and the sight of ugly "train tracks" that others had to look at. But the outcome was well worth the trouble. Seeing all that unattractive metal on my teeth at my advanced age positively inspired mothers of teenagers in braces to go for them for themselves. After all, if I wasn't too old, neither were they!

There was just one disheartening experience. A woman older than I, inspired by my braces, asked her dentist (not an orthodontist) if he thought she'd be a candidate for braces. Nasty man that he was, he told her it would be "impractical at your age." Don't ever allow anyone to shoot down your dreams and aspirations. You can always find a progressive professional to support your decision. Remember what I said about defying convention. Braces for older people may invite disapproving glances, but who cares? They are neither illegal nor immoral, so if you want your teeth in "heavy metal," go for it!

> Don't ever allow anyone to shoot down your dreams and aspirations.

At some point I want to have some cosmetic surgery, but I wanted to get my teeth in shape first. It's depressing to see women spend a lot of money on a facelift only to have it frame yellowed, crooked or missing teeth. It devalues the facelift. In going through "before" and "after" photos in cosmetic surgeons' offices, I've begun to wonder why they don't forge alliances with orthodontists. They'd be doing their cosmetic surgery patients a huge favor if they encouraged them to take care of their teeth first – or even after, for that matter. Better late than never.

Controlling your outward appearance begins with what you ingest and what you think about, believe and act upon over a long period of time. It's unfortunate to see women spend money on all kinds of creams and cosmetics trying to put off or hide the ravages of time. Yet they treat their body as if it's just a garbage can, filling it with palate-pleasing junk that is destructive and accelerates aging.

It's really pretty simple. Assuming you are not afflicted with a condition over which you have no control, if you take care of your health, exercise and drink adequate amounts of water, then your physical appearance will be great for a long period of time.

Watch your posture

Stay aware of your posture. If you are staying strong, exercising and watching your diet, you shouldn't start leaning forward. Standing tall is like the hands of a clock at 6:00. You know you are losing it when you see yourself moving to 6:10, 6:15. It's a constant struggle so stay aware. Keep your shoulders back. Sit tall, stand tall, walk tall, think tall. When you see someone with poor posture, use it as a cue to pull your shoulders back and stand straight. Cultivate a "princess persona." Visualize carrying yourself with the regal bearing of Princess Grace or Audrey Hepburn as she so elegantly carried herself in the movie "Roman Holiday." Those are my "posture" role models – find who works for you. The world will look more inviting as you stand tall, and so will you! Remember, good posture is a highly youthful characteristic.

> Remember, good posture is a highly youthful characteristic.

Make the commitment

Develop a plan to grow ageless. Visualize how you want to be and look 10 years from now. Make the plan sharp, using great detail. Write down what you will do and how you will put your plan into action.

- Do you envision yourself as slim and agile, carrying an erect posture? What will your hair, face, and teeth look like?

- How will you be dressed?

- What activities and work will engage your mind and your time?

- With whom will you be living, working or associating, and in what circumstances?

- What will you have accomplished, or be in the process of accomplishing?

- Will you have what matters most to you?

Constantly refine your future image and circumstances until they becomes so real you grow into them. Your subconscious will automatically help bring it into being. You will become what you think about most persistently, not because I say so, but because that's what actually happens. Accepting and internalizing this reality will lead you to make many positive changes in your life.

In my bedroom I have the following words of wisdom framed and in a spot where I can't avoid seeing them: "You have to think like, talk like, act like the person you would be if you had what you desire. That is the secret to realizing your dreams. If you do not become first your dream, with all its possessions, your goal will always be in the future, just out of reach."

Understanding the quality and quantity of your thoughts is an extremely powerful and elusive concept – most people miss its significance and potential. Now would be a good time to take stock of what goes on in your head. Be brutally honest with yourself and, at the same time, be kind to yourself. Don't beat yourself up if you decide you think too many negative thoughts. Acknowledge what you don't like, resolve to change and then do it. If the process is slow, it doesn't matter. You are trying, and I guarantee that eventually you will get to where you want to be if you are persistent.

Don't put it off. Start now: Don't allow yourself to believe "I don't have time to do it." You always find time to do what you really want to do. Prioritize. Develop an anti-aging program and do it each day, even when you don't feel like doing it. This is really the key to success – relentless *persistence* regardless of what is going on in your head or your life. You will fall into a routine and not only will it become easy, you'll look forward to seeing progress take place sooner than you could imagine. The rewards are too great to pass up. It's not pie-in-the-sky stuff that just sounds good on paper. I know from experience it works. *You can do it.*

> Develop an anti-aging program and do it each day, even when you don't feel like doing it. This is really the key to success – relentless *persistence* regardless of what is going on in your head or your life.

The Religion of Chronological Age

While doing research, I came across a legal case known as Torcaso v. Watkins. It was a landmark case that established belief in God was not necessary for a belief system to be considered a religion.

In thinking about how our society looks at age and the aging process, it occurred to me we do indeed have a Religion of Chronological Age, which demands a rigid code of thinking and behavior.

It's an insidious religion, because most people are unaware they are adherents or believers until it's pointed out to them. Major tenets of the religion are as follows (some have been discussed already):

☒ _Thou shall retire at 65 and look forward to a life of leisure._ Belief in this tenet is changing but still holds sway in our society. The website www.retired.com celebrates the "admired status of being retired." I looked at it and after quickly assessing the shallowness of its premise, one of the first things that popped into my mind, as I went through the site, was an old Peggy Lee song, "Is That All There Is?" Food, travel, hobbies, relationships – all neat stuff – but as a way of life? Sooner or later, it has to get boring.

☒ _Thou shall joke about thy age and refer to thyself as "old" at every opportunity. Thy friends will love thee for thy honesty because it makes them feel better about their own downward spiral._

☒ _Thou shall engage in self-talk that hastens decline such as "I must be getting old," "I'm too old to learn anything new," "I'm falling apart."_ (It's supposed to be cute and funny, but it's not. It's devastating.)

☒ _Thou shall look forward to leaving the real world and moving to a retirement village where thou can safely practice thy religion with like-minded believers._

☒ _Thou shall abdicate responsibility for thy health and welfare to thy doctor and other experts who claim to know better than thee what's best for thou. After all, it's a given that after age 65, thy brain doesn't function as well as it used to._

☒ *Thou shall start counting down to "D" or death day at age 60 if not sooner. Meaning thou shall first consider the number of years thou imagines thee has left before engaging in a long-range project.*

☒ *Thou shall take pride in referring to thyself as an "old geezer" or "old broad" and associate only with other "old geezers" or "old broads," for thee has found pleasure in the adage "misery loves company."*

☒ *Thou shall buy into the entitlement mentality and consider thyself a victim if thou cannot get what thou thinks thou is entitled to because thou are a "senior citizen."*

☒ *Thou shall join seniors-only organizations and subscribe to seniors-only publications. It's another manifestation of "misery loves company."*

☒ *Thou shall not have a relationship with another adult significantly younger than thee unless thou are a male, in which case, thou are regarded as a virile phenomenon, and thou can go on talk shows and brag about thy erectile capability.*

☒ *If thou are a woman over 50, thou certainly shall not have a relationship with a younger man unless thou are an entertainer such as Mary Tyler Moore who is married to a man 18 years younger or Tina Turner who is with a man 16 years younger.* (The grandmother of a young person I know is married to a man 30 years younger. These long-term relationships are significant and provide something for our ageist, chronologically obsessed culture to think about.)

☒ *Thou shall make repeated references to age, which gives credence to prevailing thought and conventional wisdom that says at any*

given age, thou should think and act in a manner befitting the
social or cultural expectations for that age.

These and other existing "articles of faith" which our
society buys into confirm we do indeed worship "the
numbers." We venerate Chronological Age, placing it on a high
altar and bow low before this destructive, controlling idol!

Instead of Celebrating Birthdays

Think about this: If you didn't know your chronological age,
how would you live, think and behave? (Mind you, I'm not
asking, "If you didn't know your age what age would you be?"
That question perpetuates the obsession with numbers.) If all
you had to go on was what you learned from past experiences,
your desire to consummate unfulfilled dreams, the condition of
your health, finances and personal obligations, *what would you be*
doing? Without a constant reminder of how many years you may
have left to live, *how would your life be different?*

> Do not allow
> chronolog-
> ical age to
> dictate the
> terms and
> agenda for
> your life.

Do not allow chronological age to dictate
the terms and agenda for your life. Ignore the
numbers and all the negative inferences
attached to them. Live the way you want to live,
do what you want to do and know you could "if
it weren't for my age."

As a child I can't recall the number of times
I heard my mother lament, "If only I were ten
years younger I would . . ." She lived to 92, and as much as she
accomplished, which was a lot for a woman of her era, she
forfeited so many opportunities to fulfill her dreams "because
of her age."

Don't let that happen to you. Refuse to participate in any
more birthday celebrations. Birthday parties are for kids. You
and your mother celebrated your birthday on Day One of your

life and that should be sufficient for you as an adult. This annual event is a gloomy acknowledgment of the past and a tyrannical and unnecessary reminder of what little time may be left. I stress *may* because no one knows when the final moment will occur. That alone is depressing, but what's worse is when friends send a cute but hurtful reminder of your mortality.

For example, how do you *really* feel when you receive a card with a sentiment such as this: "Hey, Babe, you are finally 50! So what if you are over the hill! Take your arthritis medicine and boogie the night away if you can stay awake past 8 PM." Sure, you giggle but you may not realize how destructive it is to your self-image and how much it accelerates your aging process. Remember, you may shrug off the silliness but your subconscious doesn't discern what's real and what isn't. You've been told you are "over the hill" by people you love and trust and whether you consciously choose to believe it or not, your subconscious believes it. It "sinks in" – takes hold and influences the evolution of how you perceive yourself, which in turn speeds up your aging process.

Perhaps friends throw a party and present you with "gifts" of ExLax™ and a bottle of Geritol™ as a reminder you are slowing down in more ways than one.

They hug you and lavish "love" on you with these "supportive" comments:

"You're really holding up well for your age, dear."

"You look a little stiff; is your arthritis bothering you, darling?"

"You took tired, sweetie. You're not overdoing it, are you?"

"Did you get your invitation to join AARP"?

"A new senior community is opening. Seems like a nice place to retire."

Oh, shit! Who needs it? Sorry about the four-letter word but there is no other way to adequately express my exasperation.

Develop a twelve-month-Put-Old-on-Hold agenda.

Not to worry. There is a better way. Instead of celebrating once a year, develop a Put-Old-on-Hold agenda for the next twelve months. Plan to do one or more things each month that will help you Put Old on Hold, then do it! Here are twelve suggestions:

Month No. 1: Cut out all greasy snack foods from your diet and watch the weight melt away. Now that's something to celebrate!

Month No. 2: Enroll in an exercise class or invest in a treadmill and watch your cardio vascular system strengthen while even more weight falls off. Isn't that more exciting than a calorie-loaded birthday party?

Month No. 3: Read a book by a nutrition guru and put into practice what makes sense to you. Then read another health-related book and another.

Month No. 4: Get a new hairstyle and color. Why wait another year to update your appearance?

Month No. 5: Replace clothing that dates you. Donate discarded items to a tax exempt organization and remember to declare it as a deduction on your income tax. You certainly can't take a deduction for a birthday party!

Month No. 6: Sign up for a computer or personal finance class at your local college or enroll in a voice or drama class. If there is a latent computer nerd or star-struck diva within you – *now is the time to go for it!*

Month No. 7: Start laying the groundwork for the dream career or job you've always wanted. Put your plan in writing, review it, refine it and add to it every day. Same time next year you will really have something to celebrate.

Month No. 8: Find more opportunities to interact with younger people of either gender. Celebrate their positive youthful qualities that will help you Put Old on Hold.

Month No. 9: Do something family, friends, custom or tradition say you are not supposed to do "at your age." If it's not illegal or immoral, *just do it!* If you must have a party, throw one to announce your intention to become a brain surgeon. Just be prepared to do it. This is not the time to be a "wannabe."

Month No. 10: Watch TV more selectively and cut the number of hours you do watch. Use the time to read or do something to help you Put Old on Hold. If you must watch TV, do it while you walk or exercise. Have you ever walked or exercised during a birthday party? (Now, there's an idea!)

Month No. 11: Volunteer at a local senior center or convalescent home. It's a perfect win-win deal. You do a good deed and get a bird's eye view of what debilitating old age is really like. It will motivate you to work your plan to Put Old on Hold.

Month No. 12: Review your accomplishments for the past months and start a new, better-than-ever plan for the next 12 months.

After you successfully complete your first Put Old on Hold year, if you haven't already done so, motivate others and invite them to join you in your monthly celebrations. You will feel the power and know you are defusing the domination of chronological age.

I have begun Put Old on Hold International, an organization designed to help women avoid premature old age, engage in lifelong productivity, and network to advance business and personal goals. (Sorry, it's not for the happily retired or those who want to be.) It's an alternative to the annual birthday celebration. It is open to all women with one stipulation regarding age: There is a "don't ask, don't tell policy" because no one's ability or aspirations may be judged on the basis of age. "Isn't she wonderful for her age" type comments are not allowed. Complaining about physical ailments is a no-no. We want to stay positive about our approach to life and our solution to problems. We help each other stay strong, focused and determined.

Although still in our infancy as an organization, this is how we operate:

Every participant makes a 12-month Put Old on Hold plan or agenda. Each woman decides what she can and will do with each month. It doesn't matter what it is as long as, in her own eyes, she's accomplishing something to Put Old on Hold.

Once a month satellite groups of twelve or fewer meet at a restaurant of their choice for a healthy lunch. We try to keep the number at twelve for each meeting so there is time for effective support and interaction. Each group has a person who records the highlights of the meeting. This information is disseminated in an e-newsletter to all participants so everyone has the same news.

We are all busy, so luncheons are limited to two hours. Quickly and briefly we relate our successes and motivate each other. We have a "discovery" session that is fun, informative and exciting. It consists of each person sharing anything she has found helpful or useful in her quest to Put Old on Hold that month. "Discovery" items are shared in two minutes or less. Anyone who wants to know more about an item can meet privately with the person offering the information. Some participants prepare their news as a handout since time is limited. Here are some typical "discoveries" that range from ridiculous to sublime:

- A particularly motivating event, personal or otherwise;
- Job openings at a new business that offer great opportunities for growth for older workers;
- A "must read" book on financial success for late bloomers;
- A new class at the local community college and why it's special;
- A new vitamin supplement and why it's great;
- A fabulous skin cream or other super cosmetic enhancement;
- A traditionally trained MD who practices integrative medicine;
- Where to find "whatever" to help Put Old on Hold.

It doesn't matter what the discovery is as long as it made a difference – large or small – for the person who offers the information. It is amazing how gratifying and empowering these monthly meetings are. They demonstrate the rewards of future-oriented thinking and living, regardless of age.

Twice a year, all satellite groups convene for an all-day whirlwind conference designed to reinforce Put Old on Hold goals and aspirations. We give awards to those who have most successfully Put Old on Hold – and a lot are given. The overall goal is to keep everyone fired up and resolute in their desire to Put Old on Hold. What an uplift bra is to the bosom, we are to each other's psyche!

You have an ageless Second Life ahead. Celebrate your life in monthly increments while fully appreciating and living each day. Experience the benefits of focused planning and sharing with others what works to Put Old on Hold. Try these, and you will never again "celebrate" another depressing birthday.

> You have an ageless Second Life ahead.

Terrific Tips
to Put Old
on Hold

This, in summary, is the essence of what you've learned. If you just read this section and not the rest of the book, you are missing the heart and soul of how to achieve agelessness. Don't cheat yourself. Go back and start at the beginning; you will be glad you did. Then you will acquire the tools, motivation and guidance you need to Put Old on Hold.

- **Your health is your most valuable possession.** Without it, nothing else matters. Not money, not sex, not power. But you can have it all with exceptional health – you can remain youthful, healthy and productive regardless of age. Believe it. Make a commitment to acquiring and maintaining your health. It's not enough to want to or simply think it might be a good idea. Action makes it so. Commitment will require changes in your lifestyle. Welcome necessary change, and know you are doing the best thing for yourself and your future.

- **Educate yourself about optimum diet and nutrition.** Gradually phase out of your life the deficient, debilitating, All American diet. Remember, just because something is advertised as "food" doesn't mean it's good for you. Don't abuse your body with what you put in your mouth. You weren't born loving greasy fries and burgers and other stuff that makes you sick and old. You are capable of making good choices. You can learn to love anything that promotes your good health. Eat less, but eat more high quality food. Ultimately you will save money as well as your health. Drink pure water – lots of it. Remaining a juicy plum instead of becoming a dried-up prune will be your reward.

- Any kind of drug abuse will short-circuit your ability to Put Old on Hold so **don't abuse your body with drugs** – not legal prescription medications nor illegal street drugs.

- **Train yourself to avoid the "count down"** (I may have only X years to live) as an excuse not to have long-range plans. Stay future oriented. Goals fuel longevity and good health. Acknowledge the reality of death with appropriate legal preparation, then get on with life and live as if you will live forever. That's right – I said forever. Think positively.

- **Traditional retirement is a fast track to decline, decrepitude and an early demise** – so don't even think about it. If you "retire" from a job and move on to something you've always wanted to do that's productive and challenging, don't call it "retirement." It's your Second Life.

- **Prioritize and maintain a structured daily schedule of essential activities** (such as exercise) to help you Put Old on Hold. Follow your schedule regardless of what happens. Don't answer the phone, don't allow interruptions and don't put up with your own silly excuses for putting it off "just this one time." Stay in control when the part of you that doesn't want you to succeed tries to take over. Thoughts such as "I don't think I'll bother today" must be immediately rebuked with "Oh yes I will!"

- **Live in an environment that includes young people.** They can be uncivilized, a pain in the neck as well as an energizing joy. In their inexperience and immaturity, they are often exquisite teachers of patience, understanding and kindness. Adopt the best of their thinking and behaviors and, in return, demonstrate the best of your experience and maturity to help them grow into wise adults. The energy and vision of goal-oriented youth can provide hope and motivation for the future.

- **Avoid certain people, seniors-only organizations and publications that give an inescapable impression "the end is near."** They have a devastating effect on your subconscious and therefore on your conscious behavior. If you routinely read publications that carry a lot of advertisements for cemeteries, cremation, adult diapers, dentures, reverse mortgages and seniors-only housing, find something else to read to broaden your perspective. These are good publications – many in the senior culture read them, rely on them and appreciate them. They just aren't for people committed to Putting Old on Hold.

- Instead, **read publications that encourage growth, challenge and productivity.** Read what will inspire, inform and motivate you to see all the opportunities available to you. Educate yourself to get the most out of your life.

- **Avoid being a practitioner, disciple or victim of the Religion of Chronological Age.** To be sure you are not a follower or believer, go back and review some of the major tenets. If you haven't read them yet, enlightenment awaits you.

- **Deliberately develop a pattern of positive self-talk.** When someone asks how you are, always reply "I'm fantastic" even if you feel awful. Tell your tales of woe only to those who are paid to listen. Friends will always be happy to see you if you avoid burdening them with your problems.

- **Choose friends carefully;** avoid those who would feed off of your youthful vitality and give nothing in return. Choose as friends those with your outlook and level of vibrancy or on whose level you would like to function.

- **Seek out role models** and copy their specific behaviors that foster growth and positive change. **Be a role model** for younger people as well as your peers. Project a genuine aura of success others will value and want to emulate.

- **Strive to maintain a quality of vibrancy.** It's a highly youthful characteristic. Let the world see the light within you. Notice the lifeless, withdrawn, seemingly angry expression on the faces of many old people. In contrast, young people project a glowing animated awareness and interest in what's going on around them. It's a gift that comes with youth. As the years go by, the gift diminishes but can be restored. You can choose to cultivate a pleasant, alive expression that will give you a more youthful appearance. It will make you feel better, too.

- **Develop a positive, uplifting and outrageous sense of humor.** If you can laugh at a "problem" you won't remember next week, or brush off most of life's "small stuff" irritations with a smile, you will stay younger much longer.

- **Defy convention if it holds you back from reaching your goal** to Put Old on Hold. Be sure you understand what this means. Think about the many subtle ways convention may sabotage a youthful, productive future. If there is something you want to do but believe you shouldn't attempt at your age, and only because it currently isn't done at your age, then just do it.

- **Revel in standing apart from the masses** of aging, conforming lemmings speeding toward the deep abyss of old age.

- **Be a rebel and a leader;** delight in running ahead of the pack, showing by example the way to agelessness. As you speed past traditional old age, reach out to others and encourage them to join you. Take them by the hand or even "under your wing" and nurture them as they develop strength and conviction. They will learn to soar agelessly on their own.

- **Encouraging others to take charge of their lives is powerful beyond imagination.** Spreading the concept of agelessness and all that it embodies (i.e., super health and a determined youthful attitude) is absolutely "viral" and has a boomerang effect. The more people you "infect" and help to live agelessly, the longer *you* will live and stay vibrantly young and healthy. There is absolutely no doubt about it. It works for me and will work for you.

- **I am so eager for you to achieve agelessness that I'd like you to do one thing for me before you close this book.** Right now – close your eyes and imagine yourself at age 60, 70 or beyond. See yourself feeling physically strong, mentally sharp, looking fantastic, full of youthful energy, anticipating wonderful things to come, doing what you want to do because you are in prime, peak condition. Feel the power you have because you've taken control of your lifestyle choices. Take this first easy step right now, do it again tomorrow, the next day and the next until it becomes an automatic part of your daily routine. Each day, visualize your future self in ever-greater detail and you will become your vision. I guarantee it, you will Put Old on Hold!

Your determination and your plan of action to Put Old on Hold are very important to help explode myths and misconceptions about "aging" and "old age." Your commitment to Put Old on Hold plays a vital role in achieving positive change. Please write to me and tell me how and what you are doing. I'd really like to hear from you. (My address is on the order page.)

> Each day visualize your future self in ever-greater detail and you will become your vision. I guarantee it, you will Put Old on Hold!

Resources

The amount of help and information available from so many sources can be overwhelming and that's the last thing you need if you are just beginning your mission to Put Old on Hold. What's listed below is a good place to start. I could list a ton of resources about which I personally know little or nothing but it wouldn't serve you well. What I provide represents what I have found helpful at this stage of my life. Over the years, I've sifted and sorted through tons of material and tried to narrow down what works best for me. Having said that, please don't stop with what's given here. You will need to go through a lot of information before you find what makes sense to you. *Let this be just the beginning of your quest.*

Books

The Antioxidant Miracle, Lester Packer, Ph.D., w/Carol Colman, John Wiley & Sons, 1999.

Drug-Induced Nutrition Depletion Handbook, Ross Pelton, et al., Natural Health Resources, 1999.

Juicy Tomatoes, Plain Truths, Dumb Lies, and Sisterly Advice About Life After 50, Susan Swartz, New Harbinger Publications, 2000.

Grow Young with HGH, Ronald Klatz, w/Carol Kahn, Harper Perennial, 1997.

Eat Right for Your Type, Peter J. D'Adamo, w/Catherine Whitney, G. P. Putnam's Sons, 1996.

Your Body's Cries For Water, F. Batmanghelidj, Global Health Solution, 1995.

Cosmetic Surgery: Before, Between and After, Susan Gail, Melange Unlimited, 2000.

Retirement is Over-Rated, Donald R. Germann, M.D., Leathers Publishing Productions, 1998.

Brain Longevity, Dharma Singh Khalsa, M.D., w/Cameron Stauth, Warner Books, 1997.

Magazines

Life Extension
1881 North 26 Street, Suite 221
Wilton Manors, FL 33305
phone: 954-561-7909
e-mail: Lemagazine@lef.org
website: http://www.lef.org

Let's Live
11050 Santa Monica Blvd.
Los Angeles, CA 90025
phone: 310-445-7500
e-mail: info@letslivemag.com
website: http://www.letsliveonline.com

Newsletters

Dr. Julian Whitaker's Health & Healing
Phillips Health
7811 Montrose Road
Potomac, MD 20859-0004
phone: 800-539-8219
website: http://www.drwhitaker.com

The Sinatra Health Report
Stephen Sinatra, M.D., F.A.C.C.
Phillips Health

7811 Montrose Road
Potomac, MD 20854-3394
phone: 800-211-7643
website: http://www.drsinatra.com

Health Sciences Institute
819 N. Charles St.
Baltimore, MD 21201
phone: 978-514-7852

Websites

http://www.knonosmedicine.com
http://www.womansage.com
http://www.minniepauz.com
http://www.susangail.com
http://www.reverseaging.org

Miscellaneous Information

Carol Maggio Facercise
6960 Eastgate Blvd.
Lebanon, TN 37090
phone: 615-449-8877

Penta Hydrate Water
Bio Hydration Research Lab., Inc.
6370 Nancy Ridge Road # 104
San Diego, CA 92121
phone: 858-452-8868
website: http://www.hydrateforlife.com

ACAM
American College for Advancement in Medicine
(To find an alternative or integrative physician)
23121 Verdugo Drive, Suite 204
Laguna Hills, CA 92653
phone: 949-583-7666, 800-532-3688

Index

A

Age-related taboos 116
Alpha lipoic acid 50
Antioxidants 49, 51
Attention Deficit Disorder
(ADD) 41
Attitude 93

B

Bottled spring water 56

C

Categories of medications 67
CBC/Chemistry Profile 65
Celebrating birthdays 131
Chemistry Profile 64
Chlorine and fluoride
facts about 55
Chronological age 12, 17
religion of 129
Cimetidine 62
Coenzyme Q10
cardio protective effect 47
Contributions to getting old 95
CoQ10 50
Cosmetic surgery 124

D

Daily schedule
how to maintain 139
Defining convention 142
Developing a plan 127
Direct to consumer (DTC) 27, 63

E

Exercise 109

F

Facial exercise 112
Fasting 25
Federal Drug Administration
(FDA) 31

G

Ginkgo 50
Goal-directed behavior 91
Group mentality phenomenon 80

H

Health care rationing 27
Human growth hormone
(HGH) 25

I

Improving your memory 33
Inventory of skills 115

J

Joint pain
supplements that help 52

L

Lifestyle/heredity ratio 24
Limiting social contact 106
Linus Pauling
vitamin C 46

M

Managed Health Care 27
Mind exercising 112
Multi-generation exposure 13
Multiple medications
    problems with 63

N

Negative self talk 99
    six deadly sins of 100

O

Optimum diet 138

P

Pharmaceutical companies
    give-aways 30
Physiological age 12
Polyphenols 51
Positive self-talk 141
Posture 111, 126
Protecting against breast cancer 53
Put Old on Hold International 135

R

Realistic perspective 117
Reasons to work: 12
Re-entering the workforce
    problems with 74
Retirement realities 71
Role models 113, 141

S

S-adenosylmethionine
    SAM-e 53
Scudder Investment Services
    survey 32

Senior-Back-to-Work Program 74
Sense of humor 117
Smoking
    suggested ways to quit 19
Soy and whey 52

T

The Conquest of Happiness
    Bertrand Russell 83
Twelve-month agenda 133

U

Unnecessary medication 60

V

Vitamin C 51
Vitamin E 50
Vitamin supplements 45, 48

W

Water
    how much is enough? 53
Water consumption 26
Water
    benefits of 57
Wellbutrin 20

Y

Yoga 111

Z

Zyban 20

Newsletter

Sometime soon I would like to offer a newsletter that will give Boomers and others the meat and motivation they need to Put Old on Hold. It will be available by subscription. If you think you would be interested, please fill out the form below and mail it to me at P.O. Box 937, Escondido, CA 2033-0937 or fax it to 760-480-9959. Right now I'm looking for amount of interest; returning the form will not commit you to anything. If the newsletter gets off the ground, the reward for your pre-publication interest will be a half price subscription for the first year. Most important: Please tell me what kind of information *you* need to help you Put Old on Hold. I want the newsletter to truly serve *your* needs and interests.

Name _____

Address _____

City, State, ZIP _____

E-mail address _____

Need a speaker for your event?

I may be able to speak to your group. Call 760-480-2710, send an e-mail to ifxpub@aol.com or write to me at P.O. Box 937, Escondido, CA 92033-0937.

Order Form

Please send the following:

Boomers *Really Can* Put Old on Hold $16.95

Boomers *Really Can* Put Old on Hold
    T-Shirt (large only) $14.95

Boomers *Really Can* Put Old on Hold
    Bumper Stickers (4) $10.00

Add $3.50 Shipping & Handling for one book

Add $5.50 Shipping & Handling for two books

Add $3.50 Shipping & Handling for each T-shirt

Bumper stickers are postage paid

Ask for bulk rates on all items

Please charge my credit card (Check one)

        ❑ Visa   ❑ Mastercard

Card # _____ Exp Date _____

Signature _____

Address _____

City/State/ZIP _____

E-mail _____

Please make checks payable and mail to:

    Image F/X Publications
    P.O. Box 937
    Escondido, CA 92033-0937

Call in your order to 760-480-2710 or fax your credit card order to 760-480-9959 or e-mail to ifxpub@aol.com